Teaching Mathematics
with the Internet

A companion Web site for this book is maintained at:

URL: http://twi.classroom.com/math/k6

Acknowledgments

Senior Product Developers: Seija Surr, Joe Todaro
Writer: Julie Kanazawa
Production Manager: Kathleen Housley
Production Designer: Sam Gorgone
Art Buyer: Jane Leibowitz
Manufacturing: Benjamin Cintas

Due to the changing nature of the Internet, site addresses and their content may vary. Great care has been put into the selection of the very best Web sites for this series. But, no long term assurances can be made regarding their suitability for school use. Please visit the companion Web site for this product for updated addresses.

Copyright © 1998 by Classroom Connect, Inc.

All rights reserved. The blackline masters in this publication are designed to be used with appropriate duplicating equipment to reproduce copies for classroom use only. Classroom Connect grants permission to classroom teachers to reproduce these masters.

Classroom Connect, Inc.
Corporate Office
2221 Rosecrans Avenue, Suite 221
El Segundo, CA 90245

Product Development Office
1241 East Hillsdale Boulevard
Foster City, CA 94404

URL: http://www.classroom.com

Email: connect@classroom.com

(800) 638-1639

All terms mentioned in this book that are known to be trademarks or service marks have been appropriately capitalized.

Printed in the United States of America.

1 2 3 4 5 6 7 8 9 10 - 02 01 00 99 98

ISBN: 1-58282-009-0

Product Code: TWI-1051

Teaching Mathematics with the Internet

Internet Lesson Plans and Classroom Activities

classroom
CONNECT
2221 Rosecrans Ave., Suite 221
El Segundo, CA 90245

TABLE OF CONTENTS

INTRODUCTION   1

LESSONS AND ACTIVITIES

GRADES K–3

    1. Dinosaur Number Hunt   2

    2. Greater and Lesser Animals   6

    3. Ancient Number Bingo   10

    4. Addition and Subtraction Monster Stories   14

    5. Pyramid Pictographs   18

    6. Planet Graph   22

    7. Musical Multiplication   26

    8. Folding Shapes   30

    9. Shapely Fractions   34

    10. Abacus Addition   38

    11. Using Common Cents   42

    12. Heads or Tails?   46

GRADES 4–6

    13. Patterns with Numbers   50

    14. Multiplication Magic   54

    15. Multicultural Multiplication   58

    16. Estimating Costs   62

    17. The Iditarod Dog Sled Race   66

    18. Athletes' Averages   70

    19. Snowflake Geometry   74

    20. Patterns and Tessellations   78

    21. Islamic Patterns   82

    22. Tangram Math   86

    23. Travel Plans   90

    24. Fractions and Food   94

    25. Measurable Improvements   98

    26. Allowable Percents   102

    27. 100% M&M's   106

    28. Lemonade Stand   110

APPENDIX

ANSWER KEY   114

LIST OF SUPPLEMENTAL WEB SITES   120

INTRODUCTION

Not more than a decade ago, the Internet was used only by a select group of organizations including government agencies and institutions of higher education. Businesses soon joined the pack and found a new way to advertise their goods and services. The Internet is now used by millions of "everyday people" around the world.

Access to the Internet is no longer limited to those with access to mainframe computers. Many users jump online from their local library or even a cyber-café. More and more households are purchasing personal computers. With the ability to connect to the online community via a telephone line, the number of users is skyrocketing. For many school districts, getting their students online is at the top of the technology agenda.

But once you have access to the Internet, how do you use it in the classroom? Sorting through the vast amount of information can be overwhelming. When will you have time to surf the Web to find sites that are appropriate? Will you be able to find information related to the topics that you need to teach? This book attempts to help you by suggesting appropriate sites and by providing you with activities that cover a variety of math topics.

Mathematics can be found all around us. Therefore, the sites used in this book are not only those you might consider math-related sites. There are sites with data about dinosaurs, planets, and athletes. There are sites with art projects and games. We hope to introduce you to a variety of ways in which the Internet can be used to enhance your curriculum.

We hope that you and your students will enjoy these activities. But more importantly, we hope that the ideas in this book spark your imagination to create other activities. Remember that the Internet is all about sharing information. So when you think of new ways to use the Internet to teach math, don't forget to share your ideas with others!

DINOSAUR NUMBER HUNT

Overview

In this lesson, students will practice writing numbers in standard form and in words. They will then use these basic number skills while collecting fun facts about dinosaurs.

Time Frame

One 45-minute session

Objectives

• Review standard form and word names for numbers.
• Practice basic reading comprehension skills.
• Learn about dinosaurs.

Materials

• Computer with Internet access
• OPTIONAL: Colored pencils, markers, or crayons

Procedure

1 Introduce the term "standard form" to students. Have them complete Step A of the Activity Sheet to practice writing the standard form and word names of numbers.

2 Have students go to the online dinosaur exhibit at The Children's Museum of Indianapolis. Visit the following Web site by typing the address on page 3 into your browser or by clicking the link on the Teaching Mathematics with the Internet Web page.

Dinosaurs at The Children's Museum of Indianapolis
URL: http://www.a1.com/children/dino.htm

This site includes information sheets on many different dinosaurs. Have students hunt for dinosaur facts on these sheets to complete Step B of the Activity Sheet. Remind students to write all numbers in standard form. Help them match the dinosaur names on the activity sheet to those on the page. Instruct them to use the "Back" button on their browser to return to the list of other dinosaur information sheets.

3 Have students complete Step C of the Activity Sheet. Students may opt to use the coloring book pictures available on each dinosaur page. Help students label their pictures with measurements found on their fact hunt.

Extensions

1 Have students write their own dinosaur fact sheets to accompany their pictures. They can use information from The Children's Museum of Indianapolis Web site or from the dinosaur information sheets at the following Web site:

Enchanted Learning: Zoom Dinosaurs
URL: http://www.EnchantedLearning.com/subjects/dinosaurs/

Mount fact sheets and pictures on large pieces of construction paper and hang them around the classroom.

2 Have the class sort their dinosaur pictures in different ways.

a. Prepare a bulletin board display where students will hang their pictures. Label one side of the board "Plant Eaters" and the other side "Meat Eaters." Have students use information from the museum Web site to help them place their pictures on the correct side of the bulletin board.

b. Students can practice comparing and ordering skills by placing their dinosaur pictures around the room from the smallest dinosaur to the largest.

3 If time permits, lead students to the Skeletons issue of the Dragonfly Web Pages to go on a virtual dinosaur dig.

Dragonfly Web Pages: Virtual Dinosaur Dig
URL: http://www.muohio.edu/dragonfly/skeletons/dig.htmlx

DINOSAUR NUMBER HUNT

NAME:_____

DATE:_____

Complete the table.

Standard Form	Word Name		Standard Form	Word Name
18				twelve
	ninety-six		84	
20			53	
11				nineteen
	forty-seven			seventy-one
38				sixty-five

Go to the following Web site.

Dinosaurs at the Children's Museum of Indianapolis
URL: http://www.a1.com/children/dino.htm

Complete the sentences using facts from the Web site. Write all numbers in standard form.

Example:
Stegosaurus protected itself with 4 to 8 spikes on the end of its tail. This dinosaur was the size of an elephant.

1. Camarasaurus grew to be _____ feet long and _____ feet high at the hips. It swallowed _____ to help grind up the plants it ate.

2. Centrosaurus grew to be _____ feet long. It defended itself with a huge _____ on its snout.

3. Pachycephalosaurus, like Centrosaurus, grew to be _____ feet long. It had a dome-shaped head with _____ inches of _____ covering its brain.

Permission granted to photocopy for classroom use only. ©1998 Classroom Connect 1-(800) 638-1639 URL: http://www.classroom.com

4. Plateosaurus bones have been found all over the world. This
_____-eater grew to be _____ feet long.

5. Scutellosaurus, or "little shield lizard," was covered with _____.
It grew to be _____ inches long.

6. Struthiomimus looked like an _____. It ate both _____ and
_____. It grew to be _____ feet tall and _____ feet long.

7. Triceratops had _____ horns on its _____, which it used to push
over tall trees. It grew to be _____ feet long and weighed up to
_____ tons.

8. Tyrannosaurus Rex was one of the most powerful _____-eating
dinosaurs. It grew to be _____ feet long, _____ feet tall, and
weighed _____ tons. Its head was _____ feet long and its teeth
were _____ inches long.

Step C

Choose one of the dinosaurs you learned about in Step B. Draw a
picture of the dinosaur and show how big it was.

Permission granted to photocopy for classroom use only. ©1998 Classroom Connect 1-(800) 638-1639   URL: http://www.classroom.com

GREATER AND LESSER ANIMALS

Overview

In this lesson, students will practice comparing and ordering numbers. They will gather information about marine life and use number sense to compare the animals.

Time Frame

One 45-minute session

Objectives

• Compare and order numbers.
• Collect and interpret data.

Materials

• Computer with Internet access

Procedure

1 Introduce the symbols for greater than (>), less than (<), and equal to (=). If necessary, illustrate the first item of Step A on the Activity Sheet to show students what it means to compare quantities. Explain that a number that is less than one number but greater than another falls between the two. Show students an example of this. Order the numbers in your example from least to greatest and from greatest to least to introduce the concept of ordering. Have students complete Step A to practice all of these skills.

2 Have students visit the following Web site by typing the address below into their browser or by clicking the link on the Teaching Mathematics with the Internet Web page.

Wyland's Marine Life Coloring Book
URL: http://www.wylandkids.com/9cb2_01.htm

This site includes fact sheets on a number of marine animals. Help students complete the table of information in Step B of the Activity Sheet. Once students have found all of the information they need on a particular animal, remind them to use the "Back" button on their browser to return to the main list. Since the weights of the humpback whale and the killer whale are given in tons, the table on the Activity Sheet shows these weights in both tons and pounds for ease of comparison. Once students have collected all of the information, have them complete Step C.

 # Extension

Students may wish to research information about other marine animals. More information about marine animals can be found at the following Web site.

Sea World's Animal Bytes
URL: http://www.seaworld.org/animal_bytes/animal_bytes.html

If students have a particular animal in mind, they can search for information about the animal at the following Web site.

Knowledge Adventure Encyclopedia
URL: http://www.adventure.com/encyclopedia/

Have students create a bulletin board display that shows drawings and information about the marine animals they found. The class should work together to hang their animals in order from smallest to largest.

GREATER AND LESSER ANIMALS

NAME: _____

DATE: _____

Use >, <, or = to compare the numbers.

1. 8____10   2. 18____13   3. 26____39

4. 63____57   5. 14____14   6. 13____5

7. 76____92   8. 36____41   9. 81____81

Write a number that is between the numbers given.

10. 38____43   11. 12____21   12. 73____68

13. 96____87   14. 44____56   15. 101____95

Write these numbers in order from least to greatest.

16. 17, 11, 32, 26, 12 _____

17. 35, 53, 33, 42, 48 _____

18. 64, 61, 67, 59, 55 _____

Use the marine animal fact sheets at this Web site to complete the table.

Wyland's Marine Life Coloring Book
URL: http://www.wylandkids.com/9cb2_01.htm

Permission granted to photocopy for classroom use only. ©1998 Classroom Connect 1-(800) 638-1639 URL: http://www.classroom.com

Marine Life Information

Animal	Length	Weight
Humpback Whale		45 tons or 90,000 pounds
Beluga		
Bottlenose Dolphin		
Green Sea Turtle		
Killer Whale		5–9 tons or 10,000–18,000 pounds
Sea Otter		
Great White Shark		

Step **C**

Use the information in your table to complete the following.

1. Which animal can grow to be 28 feet long?

_____

2. Which animal is the longest?

_____

3. Name an animal that can weigh more than a great white shark.

_____

4. Compare the lengths of sea otters and green sea turtles. What do you notice?

_____

5. List the 7 animals in order from heaviest to lightest.

_____

Permission granted to photocopy for classroom use only. ©1998 Classroom Connect 1-(800) 638-1639 URL: http://www.classroom.com

ANCIENT NUMBER BINGO

Overview

Different cultures have recorded numbers in different ways. In this lesson, students will explore number systems from Roman, Mayan, and Egyptian cultures. The class will use these numbers to play "Ancient Number Bingo."

Time Frame

One 45-minute session

Objectives

• Learn about number systems from ancient cultures.
• Develop number sense by matching numbers to clues.

Materials

• Computer with Internet access
• Scissors

Procedure

1 Explain that different cultures developed different ways to record numbers. The digits 0–9 that we use today are called Arabic numerals. Have students use the information at the following Web sites to complete the Activity Sheet on page 12.

Roman Numerals
URL: http://www.cod.edu/people/faculty/lawrence/romans00.htm

Mayan Numbers
URL: http://hanksville.phast.umass.edu/yucatan/mayamath.html

Egyptian Numbers
URL: http://eyelid.ukonline.co.uk/ancient/numbers.htm

Ask students where they have seen Roman numerals used. Help them understand that the order of the numerals determines the total value of the number. Go to the following Web site to convert any number to a Roman numeral.

Roman Numeral Converter
URL: http://www.ivtech.com/roman/

Mayan numbers greater than 19 are more complicated to show using symbols since this number system is base 20. Encourage students to only use numbers from 0–19 on their cards.

Explain that Egyptian numbers are much like our digits. They can be combined to show large numbers. For example the symbol for 11 is made up of the symbol for 10 and symbol for 1.

❷ Once the students have filled in their Ancient Number Bingo cards, have them cut out the letter markers. Explain that in this game, you will call out numbers or number clues by letter. Students must be sure to use the correct marker for each clue. Only one number on a card can be marked per clue. Winners must get 5 in a row. Winners should use the letters on the markers to prove that their numbers match the clues. Here are some sample number clues. Make up some of your own and sprinkle in a few simple numbers in between. Don't forget to keep track of the clues you call out by letter so that you can verify winning cards!

- Mark a number that is less than 5.
- Mark a number that uses more than one type of symbol.
- Mark a number that is greater than 100.
- Mark a number that is between 20 and 30.
- Mark a number that shows how many students are in our class.
- Mark a number that is less than 50.
- Mark a number that is between 75 and 85.
- Mark a number that is greater than or equal to 1,000.

ANCIENT NUMBER BINGO

NAME: _____

DATE:_____

Learn how people in other cultures wrote numbers. Then use numbers from other cultures to play Bingo!

Go to this Web site to see how the Romans wrote numbers.

Roman Numerals
URL: http://www.cod.edu/people/faculty/lawrence/romans00.htm

Write the Roman numerals for each of these.

1. 3_____   2. 8_____   3. 10_____

4. 24_____   5. 39_____   6. 51_____

7. Write 8 Roman numerals on the "Ancient Number Bingo" card.

Go to this Web site to see how the Mayans wrote numbers from 0 to 19.

Mayan Numbers
URL: http://hanksville.phast.umass.edu/yucatan/mayamath.html

Write the Mayan numbers for each of these.

8. 5_____   9. 12_____   10. 18_____

11. 7 _____   12. 4_____   13. 9_____

14. Write 8 Mayan numbers on your bingo card. Use only numbers
    from 0 to 19.

Go to this Web site to see how the Egyptians wrote numbers.

Egyptian Numbers
URL: http://eyelid.ukonline.co.uk/ancient/numbers.htm

Permission granted to photocopy for classroom use only. ©1998 Classroom Connect   1-(800) 638-1639   URL: http://www.classroom.com

Draw the Egyptian numbers for each of these.

15. 2_____   16. 12_____   17. 23_____

18. 110_____   19. 204_____   20. 56_____

21. Fill in the rest of your bingo card with Egyptian numbers. Try to use different numbers from those shown in Roman numerals and Mayan numbers.

Ancient Number Bingo

Fill in your bingo card with numbers from the Roman, Mayan, and Egyptian cultures.

Cut out the letter markers and play "Ancient Number Bingo" with your class. Try to get 5 in a row. Be sure your numbers match all of the clues.

		FREE SPACE		

A	B	C	D	E	F	G	H	I	J	K	L	M
N	O	P	Q	R	S	T	U	V	W	X	Y	Z

Permission granted to photocopy for classroom use only. ©1998 Classroom Connect 1-(800) 638-1639 URL: http://www.classroom.com

ADDITION AND SUBTRACTION MONSTER STORIES

Overview

In this lesson, students will deepen their conceptual understanding of addition and subtraction while practicing basic facts. They will solve and write monster story problems.

Time Frame

One 45-minute session

Objectives

- Develop conceptual understanding of addition and subtraction.
- Identify the appropriate operation and write the number sentence for a given problem.
- Practice basic addition and subtraction facts.

Materials

- Computer with Internet access
- OPTIONAL: Colored pencils, markers, or crayons
- Talker plug in (optional for Macintosh users)
  URL: http://www.mvpsolutions.com/PlugInSite/Talker.html
- Apple's text-to-speech technology (optional for Macintosh users)
  URL: http://speech.apple.com/ptk/ptk.html

Procedure

1 Discuss what actions students think of when they add and subtract. It may help students to think of addition as putting groups together. Subtraction can involve taking away, finding a missing part of a given whole, or even comparing groups. Have students complete Part A of the Activity Sheet.

2 Have students solve the story problems at the site below. Visit the following site by typing in the address below or by clicking the link on the Teaching Mathematics with the Internet Web page.

Monster Math
URL: http://www.lifelong.com/lifelong_universe/AcademicWorld/
        MonsterMath/default.html

This site can be viewed in English, Spanish, or Italian. Macintosh users who choose to open the site with sound must be sure to have the appropriate plug-ins listed in the Materials list. If you are a PC user or if you want to open the site in English without sound, you can go directly to the following Web site.

Monster Math: English with No Speech
URL: http://www.lifelong.com/lifelong_universe/AcademicWorld/
        MonsterMath/NTEng/default.html

Once students have chosen the language they want, have them click *Let's Find a Monster*. After they have read the instructions, they should click *Let's Join the Monster Math Surprise Party* to begin the story. Some students may need help with the problem involving odd and even numbers.

3 Have students write their own monster stories. Stories should include at least 4 different addition and subtraction problems. Students can use the monster story pages on the Activity Sheet to write problems and draw pictures. Encourage students to write different types of problems as discussed at the beginning of the lesson.

Extension

1 The monster story pages can be cut out, folded, and stapled together to make a book. As an alternative, the following Web site has instructions for making a 6-page book out of a paper grocery bag. Monster story pages can be cut out and mounted in the book.

Make a Paper Bag Book
URL: http://www.arts.ufl.edu/art/rt_room/bag_book/make_a_book.html

2 The site listed below provides interactive practice for those interested in sharpening their basic addition and subtraction skills.

Math Baseball
URL: http://www.funbrain.com/math/

ADDITION AND SUBTRACTION MONSTER STORIES

NAME:_____

DATE:_____

| Step | A |

Circle the operation you would use to solve each monster problem. Then write a number sentence.

1. Yurka bought 15 sprift cookies. She gave 6 to her sister. How many sprift cookies does Yurka have left?

   Add   Subtract

   _____

2. Klora has 12 toes. Zondi has 7 toes. How many more toes does Klora have than Zondi?

   Add   Subtract

   _____

3. Frava collects moon rocks. He had 8 rocks. He found 4 more. How many moon rocks does Frava have now?

   Add   Subtract

   _____

4. Murg has 16 fingers all together. There are 8 fingers on one hand. How many fingers are on Murg's other hand?

   Add   Subtract

   _____

Permission granted to photocopy for classroom use only. ©1998 Classroom Connect 1-(800) 638-1639 URL: http://www.classroom.com

Go to this Web site to solve more problems about monsters.

Monster Math
URL: http://www.lifelong.com/lifelong_universe/AcademicWorld/
 MonsterMath/default.html

Step **C** **Monster Story Pages**

Write your own monster story. Include at least 4 different addition and subtraction problems. You may draw pictures to help tell your story.

Permission granted to photocopy for classroom use only. ©1998 Classroom Connect   1-(800) 638-1639   URL: http://www.classroom.com

PYRAMID PICTOGRAPHS

Overview

In this lesson, students will make and interpret pictographs to help them learn about basic nutrition information. They will use what they learned to create a personalized food guide.

Time Frame

One 45-minute session

Objectives

- Make, interpret, and compare pictographs.
- Learn about the Food Guide Pyramid.

Materials

- Computer with Internet access
- OPTIONAL: Colored pencils or markers

Procedure

1 Have students go to the following Web site to read information about the Food Guide Pyramid.

The Food Guide Pyramid
URL: http://www.kidsfood.org/f_pyramid/pyramid.html

Discuss the basics of the pyramid, such as the 5 food groups and the suggested number of servings for each group. Have students click *Start* to build the Food Guide Pyramid. Once they have completed the activity, ask them to print the "Congratulations" page or to keep it on the screen.

2 Help students use the table on the "Congratulations" page to make a pictograph that shows the number of servings of each food group that they should eat. Students should decide on a symbol and fill in the key for their pictograph. Since the number of servings for each food group is small, suggest that each symbol equal 1 or 2 servings.

Help students select information from the correct column of the table. When the number of servings is given as a range, help them select a number in the middle of the range that seems appropriate. Discuss reasons for giving ranges. Ask them to think about the number of servings they eat in comparison to an adult.

3 Have students list the foods they eat on a typical day. Students who have difficulty generalizing can list the foods eaten on the previous day. Discuss serving sizes to help them record the total servings for each food group. Use the information at the following Web site to help.

What Counts as a Serving?
URL: http://www.agr.state.nc.us/cyber/kidswrld/nutrition/pyramid.htm

Have students make a pictograph of the foods they eat. Remind them to decide on a symbol and to fill in the key for their graph.

4 Once students have finished both pictographs, have them answer the questions in Step C of the Activity Sheet. For examples of foods in each food group, go to the following Web site.

Food Facts
URL: http://www.kidsfood.org/f_facts/grpslist.html

Extensions

1 A week or more after completing this lesson, ask students to make another pictograph showing what they eat on a typical day. Have them write about what they've done differently since learning about the Food Guide Pyramid.

2 Once students are familiar with the Food Guide Pyramid, they might enjoy the "Rate Your Plate" and "Winning Choices" activities at the Kids Food Cyberclub Web site.

Rate Your Plate
URL: http://www.kidsfood.org/rate_plate/rate.html

Winning Choices
URL: http://www.kidsfood.org/choices/winning/winning.html

PYRAMID PICTOGRAPHS

NAME:_____

DATE:_____

Step A

1. Go to this Web site to build a Food Guide Pyramid.

   Food Guide Pyramid
   URL: http://www.kidsfood.org/f_pyramid/pyramid.html

2. When you've completed your pyramid, you will see a chart of suggested servings. Make a pictograph to show the number of servings of each food group that you should eat each day.

My Food Guide Pictograph

Bread, cereal, rice, and pasta												
Vegetables												
Fruits												
Meat, pultry, fish, dry beans, eggs, nuts												
Milk, yogurt, and cheese												

Each   =_____servings

Step B

1. Think about what you eat on a typical day. Use the table on page 21 to list foods you might eat. At the bottom of each column, record the number of servings you've shown.

Permission granted to photocopy for classroom use only. ©1998 Classroom Connect   1-(800) 638-1639   URL: http://www.classroom.com

Bread, cereal, rice and pasta	Vegetables	Fruits	Meat, Pultry, fish, dry beans, eggs, and nuts	Milk, yogurt, and cheese
Total Servings: _____	Total Servings: _____	Total Servings: _____	Total Servings: _____	Total Servings: _____

2. Use the information from your table to make a pictograph.

What I Eat in a Day

Bread, cereal, rice, and pasta														
Vegetables														
Fruits														
Meat, pultry, fish, dry beans, eggs, nuts														
Milk, yogurt, and cheese														

Each   =_____servings

Step   C

Use the pictographs you made to answer the questions.

1. What types of foods do you eat the most? The least?

_____

2. What types of food should you eat more often? Less often? Compare your pictographs to decide.

_____

Permission granted to photocopy for classroom use only. ©1998 Classroom Connect 1-(800) 638-1639 URL: http://www.classroom.com

PLANET GRAPH

Overview

In this lesson, students will make and interpret bar graphs using data about the number of moons around each planet in our solar system.

Time Frame

One 45-minute session

Objectives

• Make and interpret bar graphs.
• Learn about moons in our solar system.

Materials

• Computer with Internet access
• OPTIONAL: Colored pencils or markers

Procedure

1 Have students go to the following Web site. To access the data on moons in our solar system, follow the instructions below or visit the site by clicking the link on the Teaching Mathematics with the Internet Web page.

Windows to the Universe
URL: http://www.windows.umich.edu/

• Click *Enter the Site*.
• Click *Our Solar System*.

- Select the Beginner level at the top of the page and then click *Solar System Facts*.
- Click *Table of Planets*. Have students scroll down to the bottom of the table to see the number of moons for each planet.

This site contains graphics that can take a long time to load. If your Internet connection is 28.8 kbs or slower, you may want to cache the site before class. You can also bypass the loading of graphics by clicking text menu items.

2 Have students collect information on the number of moons from the "Table of Planets." Explain that bar graphs can help us to visualize data. Have students make a bar graph of the data they collected. Remind students to include labels for each axis as well as a title for their graph. Once they have completed their bar graphs, have them answer the questions on the Activity Sheet.

Extension

The following information on the lengths of days was collected from the "Planetary Facts" sheets for each planet at the Windows to the Universe Web site. If you want students to practice converting units of time from days and hours to minutes, have them go to the fact sheet for each planet and collect their own data. Students who are familiar with decimals can use the day lengths given in the "Table of Planets." Have students work together to make a bar graph of the data. Discuss what scale they might use.

Planet	Length of Day in Earth Minutes
Mercury	253,440
Venus	168,480
Earth	1,440
Mars	1,447
Jupiter	595
Saturn	614
Uranus	1,034
Neptune	1,026
Pluto	9,180

PLANET GRAPH

NAME:_____

DATE:_____

Go to this Web site. Follow your teacher's instructions to get to the "Table of Planets" page.

Windows to the Universe
URL: http://www.windows.umich.edu/

1. Record the number of moons that each planet has.

Planet	Number of Moons
Mercury	
Venus	
Earth	
Mars	
Jupiter	
Saturn	
Uranus	
Neptune	
Pluto	

2. Make a bar graph of the data you collected. Be sure to label each axis and include a title for your graph.

Permission granted to photocopy for classroom use only. ©1998 Classroom Connect   1-(800) 638-1639   URL: http://www.classroom.com

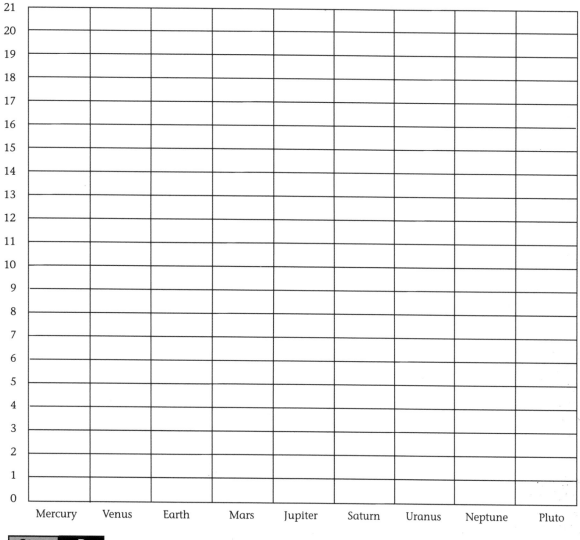

	Mercury	Venus	Earth	Mars	Jupiter	Saturn	Uranus	Neptune	Pluto
21									
20									
19									
18									
17									
16									
15									
14									
13									
12									
11									
10									
9									
8									
7									
6									
5									
4									
3									
2									
1									
0									

Step   B

Use the data you collected and your bar graph to answer each question.

1. Which planet has the most moons?

   _____

2. Which planets have the fewest moons?

   _____

3. How many more moons does Jupiter have than Earth?

   _____

4. Which planet has the same number of moons as Earth?

   _____

Permission granted to photocopy for classroom use only. ©1998 Classroom Connect   1-(800) 638-1639   URL: http://www.classroom.com

MUSICAL MULTIPLICATION

Overview

In this lesson, students will focus on basic fact memorization strategies. They will work together to share their ideas through poetry or song.

Time Frame

Two 45-minute sessions

Objectives

- Practice basic multiplication facts.
- Communicate memorization strategies.

Materials

- Computer with Internet access
- RealAudio plug in (optional)
  URL: http://www.realaudio.com
- Quicktime plug in (optional)
  URL: http://quicktime.apple.com/sw/sw3.html

Procedure

1 Have students fill in as much of the multiplication table as they can. Discuss patterns they notice as they fill in the table. Have them write about patterns in the table or strategies they used. Ask them to use the patterns to help complete the table.

② Organize students into teams of 3 or 4. You may choose to assign each team a group of multiplication facts from the numbers 2 through 9 or have them decide. Ensure that each team chooses a different group of facts. Each team should list the patterns and methods its members noticed for its group of facts.

③ Have the students go to the following Web site and select the song for their team's fact group.

Multiplication Rock
URL: http://genxtvland.simplenet.com/SchoolHouseRock/
    multiplication.hts?lo

If the RealAudio plug in is available, have the students listen to the song. Quicktime movies are available at the site but may take a long time to load.

Have each team discuss patterns or strategies mentioned in the song. Ask students to talk about any methods they found that weren't mentioned in the song. Have teams work together to create their own multiplication fact song or poem. Suggest that students write new lyrics to familiar tunes. Students should be sure to include some or all of the fact strategies they used. Have each team present its song or poem to the rest of the class.

Extensions

① Students who want to practice basic multiplication facts online can go to the following Web site. Be sure to have them select the easy level of multiplication before starting.

Math Baseball
URL: http://www.funbrain.com/math/

② The Vedic Square was described in the *Vedas*, one of the oldest Indian texts. Each number in the Vedic square is the "Vedic sum" of the product in a multiplication table. To find the Vedic sum of a number, continuously add its digits until the sum is 9 or less. The Vedic sum of 56 is found by adding $5 + 6 = 11$ and $1 + 1 = 2$. Therefore, 2 is the Vedic sum of 56. A complete Vedic square can be found at the following Web site.

Vedic Square
URL: http://www.amulet.co.uk/symbols/kamea/vedic.html

Have students make a Vedic Square on square grid paper. Have them use different colored pencils or markers to connect the centers of squares with the same Vedic sum. Have them talk about the geometric patterns they find.

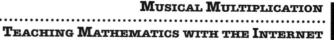

MUSICAL MULTIPLICATION

NAME:_____

DATE:_____

1. Fill in as many products as you can in this multiplication table.

×	1	2	3	4	5	6	7	8	9
1									
2									
3									
4									
5									
6									
7									
8									
9									

2. Write about any of the strategies that you used to fill in the table.
   Then describe any patterns you notice in the table.

   _____

   _____

Permission granted to photocopy for classroom use only. ©1998 Classroom Connect   1-(800) 638-1639   URL: http://www.classroom.com

3. If you haven't completed the table, try using the patterns you found to help you find the missing products.

_____

_____

Step   B

With your teammates, decide on a group of multiplication facts for a number from 2 through 9. Have each person share the patterns and strategies he or she noticed for that number. Go to the following Web site and select the song for your number.

Multiplication Rock
URL: http://genxtvland.simplenet.com/SchoolHouseRock/
      multiplication.hts?lo

1. What fact patterns or strategies does the song mention?

_____

_____

_____

2. What other patterns or strategies did your teammates come up with?

_____

_____

_____

3. Help other students memorize facts. Work with your teammates to write a song or a poem. Include some or all of the patterns and strategies each team member found. Be prepared to present your song or poem to the rest of the class.

_____

_____

_____

Permission granted to photocopy for classroom use only. ©1998 Classroom Connect 1-(800) 638-1639 URL: http://www.classroom.com

FOLDING SHAPES

Overview

Geometric shapes and symmetry permeate origami, the Japanese art of paper folding. In this lesson, students will fold a simple origami figure. They will examine the figure and the folds for shapes and symmetry.

Time Frame

One 45-minute session

Objectives

- Identify common geometric shapes such as squares, rectangles, and triangles.
- Explore combinations of shapes that make other shapes.
- Identify lines of symmetry.

Materials

- Computer with Internet access
- Scissors
- OPTIONAL: Colored pencils or markers

Procedure

1 Discuss the characteristics of basic shapes such as squares, rectangles, triangles, and circles. Ask students where they can find these shapes in the world around them. Introduce origami as the art of Japanese paper folding. Explain that this art form has existed for over 1,000 years. Originally only religious leaders could afford to fold paper as it was expensive and difficult to find. Now that paper is available to all, origami is enjoyed by people of all ages around the world. Explain that in this activity, students will be looking for shapes in an origami samurai figure named Yakko.

2 Have students cut out the square on page 33. Visit the following Web site by typing in the address below into your browser or by clicking the link on the Teaching Mathematics with the Internet Web page. This site may take time to download. If your Internet connection is 28.8 kbs or slower, you may want to cache the site before class.

Yakko
URL: http://jw.nttam.com:80/KIDS/SCHOOL/ART/origami/
kids_origami_yakko.html

3 Guide students through each of the steps. To help students find the center of the square, suggest that they fold the paper in half vertically and horizontally before starting. Have them list any shapes they find while folding Yakko.

Origami masters often unfold their creations to examine the many shapes and patterns in the folds themselves. For more on this topic, go to the following Web site.

Origami Folding Patterns
URL: http://ccwf.cc.utexas.edu/~vbeatty/origami/learning/pattern.html

Have students carefully unfold their papers and help them record the folds on the grid provided. Ask students to explain why there aren't any circles in their folds. Have them describe the shapes on their grids.

4 Introduce the concept of symmetry. Discuss the four lines of symmetry in a single square. Show some non-examples to help strengthen students' conceptual understanding. Have them look for symmetry in Yakko.

Extension

The origami crane is a symbol of peace. Share the story of *Sadako and the Thousand Paper Cranes* by Eleanor Coerr. The following Web site has instructions for this elegant origami form.

How to Fold a Crane
URL: http://www.rose.brandeis.edu/users/peisach/ vcrane.html

FOLDING SHAPES

NAME: _____

DATE: _____

How can a square piece of paper be turned into the form of a person? Cut out the square on page 33 and then go to this Web site to learn how.

Yakko
URL: http://jw.nttam.com:80/KIDS/SCHOOL/ART/origami/
        kids_origami_yakko.html

1. What shapes did you notice as you folded Yakko?

   _____

   _____

2. Carefully unfold your paper and look at all of the folds. Use this grid to draw a picture of the folds.

Permission granted to photocopy for classroom use only. ©1998 Classroom Connect 1-(800) 638-1639 URL: http://www.classroom.com

Cut out the square and use it to fold Yakko.

Permission granted to photocopy for classroom use only. ©1998 Classroom Connect   1-(800) 638-1639   URL: http://www.classroom.com

SHAPELY FRACTIONS

Overview

In this lesson, students will explore fraction concepts using pattern block shapes. They will explore how the same shape can represent different fractional amounts depending on how the unit is defined.

Time Frame

One 45-minute session

Objectives

- Explore fractional relationships among shapes.
- Write fractions.

Materials

- Computer with Internet access
- Colored pencils or markers
- OPTIONAL: Pattern blocks; scissors; Java-capable browser (Netscape 3.0+ or Explorer 3.0+)

Procedure

1 Have students go to the following Web site.

Fraction Shapes
URL: http://math.rice.edu/~lanius/Patterns/

Have them write the names of the 4 pattern block shapes in Step A of the Activity Sheet. Students may print, color, and cut out the shapes available at the following Web site.

Shapes
URL: http://math.rice.edu/~lanius/images/4_polygo.gif

You may wish to have students use wood or plastic pattern blocks if available. If your browser supports Java, students may print the page of instructions and go to the following site to explore the shapes online.

Pattern Blocks
URL: http://www.best.com/~ejad/java/patterns/patterns_j.shtml

2 Once students have explored the shapes, have them complete Step B to determine the relationships among the shapes. For questions 1–6, students should trace their shapes or sketch pictures on the Activity Sheet to record their work. For questions 7–10, have students write the fraction that each shape represents. Advise them to pay special attention to which shape equals 1 whole. Questions 6 and 10 may be a little tricky. For help with these items, read the explanation on the following Web page.

Fraction Shapes: Teacher Notes
URL: http://math.rice.edu/~lanius/Patterns/notes.html

Extension

The Fraction Shapes Web site includes other pattern block activities. The following activities explore concepts of adding and subtracting fractions using shapes instead of algorithms. You may go to these activities from the Fraction Shapes page or by typing in the addresses into your browser.

Fun Fractions
URL: http://math.rice.edu/~lanius/Patterns/add.html

Drawing Fun Fractions
URL: http://math.rice.edu/~lanius/Patterns/draw.html

SHAPELY FRACTIONS

NAME:_____

DATE:_____

Step **A**

Write the name of each shape.

1.	2.	3.	4.

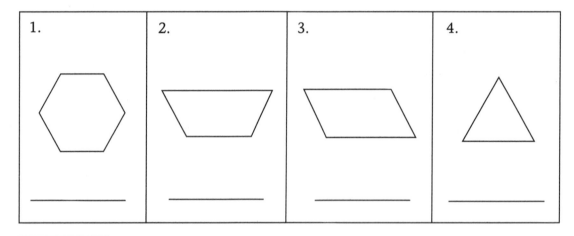

Step **B**

Go to this Web site.

Fraction Shapes
URL: http://math.rice.edu/~lanius/Patterns/

Scroll down to *Determining the Relations*. You will find questions there.
Record your answers below and draw pictures to show your work.

1.	2.

Permission granted to photocopy for classroom use only. ©1998 Classroom Connect 1-(800) 638-1639 URL: http://www.classroom.com

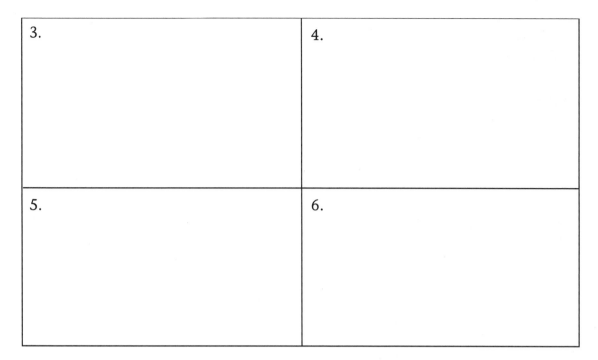

3.	4.
5.	6.

Record your answers for questions 7–10 below. Write the fraction that each piece shows. Remember to check which piece equals 1 whole.

7.

8.

9.

10.

Permission granted to photocopy for classroom use only. ©1998 Classroom Connect   1-(800) 638-1639   URL: http://www.classroom.com

ABACUS ADDITION

 ## Overview

The abacus has been used to help calculate numbers for thousands of years. In this lesson students will learn how to represent numbers on an abacus. They will use an online abacus to add numbers.

 ## Time Frame

One 45-minute session

 ## Objectives

- Learn about the abacus.
- Compose and decompose numbers.

 ## Materials

- Computer with Internet access
- SPECIAL BROWSER NEEDS: Java-capable Browser
  (Netscape 3.0+ or Explorer 3.0+)

Procedure

1 Go to the following Web site to learn about the history and use of the abacus.

The Abacus
URL: http://www.ee.ryerson.ca:8080/~elf/abacus/

Review the composition and decomposition of numbers using the place value system. For example, remind students that they can think of 345 as 3 hundreds, 4 tens, and 5 ones. Explain to students that the columns of beads on an abacus relate to the same place value columns (1, 10, 100 and so on) we use to write numbers. However, the abacus also makes use of groups of 5 to show numbers. Have students complete the table on the Activity Sheet to practice composing and decomposing numbers as you would on an abacus.

2 Have students complete items 7–12 on the Activity Sheet by using the Chinese abacus at the following Web site.

Abacus Addition
URL: http://www.ee.ryerson.ca:8080/~elf/abacus/aaddition.html

At the top of this online abacus, students can view the number shown in standard form. Have them check this readout to make sure they place the beads correctly.

3 Review the instructions for adding numbers on an abacus given at the Abacus Addition Web site. Explain to students that the most important thing to remember when adding numbers on an abacus is that beads in each column are regrouped when a sum or 5 or 10 is reached. Have students use the Chinese abacus to complete the problems on the Activity Sheet.

Activity
Sheet
10

ABACUS ADDITION

NAME: _____

DATE: _____

An abacus is a type of calculator that uses beads instead of batteries. Go to the following Web site to learn more about the abacus.

The Abacus
URL: http://www.ee.ryerson.ca:8080/~elf/abacus/

Write how many of each type of bead you would use to show each number on an abacus.

		10	5	1
1.	4			
2.	7			
3.	11			
4.	5			
5.	20			
6.	16			

Use the Chinese abacus at the following Web site to show each number. Draw beads below to record what you did.

Abacus Addition
URL: http://www.ee.ryerson.ca:8080/~elf/abacus/aaddition.html

7.   34

8.   96

40 **ABACUS ADDITION**

Permission granted to photocopy for classroom use only. ©1998 Classroom Connect 1-(800) 638-1639 URL: http://www.classroom.com

9.   120

10.   157

11.   218

12.   1,263

Use the Chinese abacus to do each addition problem. Draw beads to show each sum.

13.   31 + 43 = _____

14.   57 + 12 = _____

15.   86 + 32 = _____

16.   64 + 95= _____

Permission granted to photocopy for classroom use only. ©1998 Classroom Connect   1-(800) 638-1639   URL: http://www.classroom.com

Using Common Cents

Overview

In this lesson, students will practice making change. They will explore different ways to make the same amount using different combinations of coins and bills.

Time Frame

One 45-minute session

Objectives

• Make change for amounts under $5.00
• Identify different ways to show the same amount of money.

Materials

• Computer with Internet access
• OPTIONAL: play money (pennies, nickels, dimes, quarters, $1 bills, and $5 bills)

Procedure

❶ Describe the count-on strategy for making change. For example, ask students how much change a customer should receive when using a $1 bill to pay for an item that costs $0.36. Begin with the cost of the item and count-on by coin amounts until $1.00 is reached. The total change is $0.64 (four pennies, one dime, two quarters).

Students may either use the count-on strategy or subtract to complete Step A on the Activity Sheet.

2 Explain that often there's more than one way to make change. In the example above, 4 pennies, 2 nickels, and 2 quarters would also provide the correct change. Help students create different combinations of coins and bills in Step B. For an extra challenge, suggest that one of the combinations use the fewest possible coins and bills.

3 Have students go to the following Web site to play the Cash Register Game.

The Cash Register Game
URL: http://www.funbrain.com/cashreg/index.html

Make sure students begin with the easy level of difficulty. Remind them that they must enter the number of coins in the boxes, not the money amounts.

Activity
Sheet
11

USING COMMON CENTS

NAME:_____

DATE:_____

It's important to make sure you receive the correct change when you go shopping. Try making change yourself.

Step   A

How much change should be given?

	Cost of Item	Paid With	Amount of Change
1.	$0.45	$1.00	
2.	$0.63	$1.00	
3.	$3.84	$5.00	
4.	$2.35	$5.00	
5.	$1.21	$5.00	
6.	$1.52	$2.00	
7.	$2.79	$3.00	
8.	$1.18	$2.00	

Explain how you would decide the change each customer should receive.

9. Joey bought a kite for $4.85. He paid with a $5 bill.

_____

10. Linda bought a sandwich for $3.98. She paid with a $5 bill.

_____

Permission granted to photocopy for classroom use only. ©1998 Classroom Connect   1-(800) 638-1639   URL: http://www.classroom.com

11. Tasha bought a cup of lemonade for $0.73. She paid with a $1 bill.

_____

12. Devin bought a notebook for $2.15. He paid with $3.00.

_____

The same amount of change can be given using different combinations of coins and bills. Decide how much change should be given. List at least 3 different combinations for each amount.

	Cost of Item	Paid With	Amount of Change	Pennies	Nickels	Dimes	Quarters	$1 Bills
1.	$0.36	$1.00						
2.	$0.83	$1.00						
3.	$3.45	$5.00						
4.	$1.57	$5.00						
5.	$2.92	$5.00						
6.	$1.64	$2.00						

Go to this Web site to play the Cash Register Game!

The Cash Register Game
URL: http://www.funbrain.com/cashreg/index.html

Permission granted to photocopy for classroom use only. ©1998 Classroom Connect 1-(800) 638-1639 URL: http://www.classroom.com

HEADS OR TAILS?

Overview

In this lesson, students will explore probability concepts. They will make predictions and conduct experiments to test their predictions. Students will then use what they learned to explore fairness in a simple game.

Time Frame

One 45-minute session

Objectives

- Classify events as certain, impossible, likely, or unlikely.
- Explore the concept of equal likelihood.
- Make and test predictions.
- Conduct experiments and analyze outcomes.

Materials

- Computer with Internet access

Procedure

❶ Describe events such as rainy weather or winning a lottery as certain, likely, unlikely, or impossible. Have students give other examples of each. Ask them to look at their classmates and then complete Step A of the Activity Sheet. If time permits, arrange the students in a circle around the room and try the experiment.

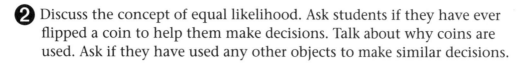

❷ Discuss the concept of equal likelihood. Ask students if they have ever flipped a coin to help them make decisions. Talk about why coins are used. Ask if they have used any other objects to make similar decisions.

Have students predict the outcome of a single coin toss as well as 50 tosses of a coin. Have them go to the following Web site to conduct the coin flipping experiment in Step B.

The Coin Flipping Page
URL: http://shazam.econ.ubc.ca/flip/

Help students collect results from classmates and record the totals in the table. Discuss how individual and class results compare to their predictions.

❸ Organize students into pairs. Have each pair designate one player as "heads" and the other as "tails." Pairs should use the above Web site to flip 50 coins. The player who has the most flips in his or her favor initials any square on the grid. Once the grid is complete, have students answer items 1–4.

HEADS OR TAILS?

NAME:_____

DATE:_____

Step A

Look around at your classmates. Suppose you stood in the middle of the room with your eyes closed and everyone in the class stood in a circle around you. If you spun around, stopped, and opened your eyes who would you see?

Use words like *certain, likely, unlikely* and *impossible* to describe the chances that the person in front of you...

Has short hair: Is wearing orange:

Is wearing jeans: Is wearing a T-shirt:

Has shoes on: Is wearing a watch:

Step B

Suppose you flip a coin to decide who will go first in a game. What do you think the chances are that the coin will land with its head up? What do you think would happen if you flipped the coin 50 times?

Use the coins at this Web site to test your predictions.

The Coin Flipping Page
URL: http://shazam.econ.ubc.ca/flip/

1. Decide which coin you would like to flip.

2. Enter 1 to flip 1 coin and click to start flipping. Record the results. Share your results with your classmates and record the class totals.

3. Click the "Back" button on your browser and flip 50 coins. Record your results and the class results.

Permission granted to photocopy for classroom use only. ©1998 Classroom Connect   1-(800) 638-1639   URL: http://www.classroom.com

Number of Coins Flipped	My Results	Class Results
1	_____ Heads _____ Tails	_____ Heads _____ Tails
50	_____ Heads _____ Tails	_____ Heads _____ Tails

Step C

Play "Heads or Tails?" with a partner. Decide who will be "heads" and who will be "tails." Flip 50 coins using the Web site. The winning player initials any square on the grid. If the results are equal, both players should mark a square. Continue until the grid is filled.

1. Who filled in the most squares?

_____

2. Do you think this game was fair? Why or why not?

_____

3. Play the game again. Who filled in the most squares this time?

_____

4. Explain what you think would happen if you played the game 10 times.

_____

HEADS OR TAILS?

49

Permission granted to photocopy for classroom use only. ©1998 Classroom Connect 1-(800) 638-1639 URL: http://www.classroom.com

PATTERNS WITH NUMBERS

Overview

Looking for and analyzing patterns is a key mathematical skill. In this lesson, students will describe and extend number patterns. They will analyze the famous Fibonacci sequence and explore the existence of this pattern in nature.

Time Frame

One 45-minute session

Objectives

• Practice identifying and extending number patterns.
• Learn about the Fibonacci sequence.

Materials

• Computer with Internet access

Procedure

1 Lead a class discussion on patterns. Ask students about patterns they've seen or heard. Discuss the difference between patterns that repeat and those that grow. Explain that the focus of this lesson is on number patterns.

Visit the following Web site by typing the address below into your browser or by clicking the link on the Teaching Mathematics with the Internet Web page. Read about the rabbit problem that Fibonacci used to describe his sequence.

Fibonacci's Rabbits
URL: http://www.mcs.surrey.ac.uk/Personal/R.Knott/Fibonacci/
   fibnat.html#Rabbits

Share this problem with the class. Help students understand how Fibonacci solved it by showing them the diagram on the page. Have students complete Step A of the Activity Sheet.

❸ Tell students that one of the reasons that this number pattern is so popular is its existence in nature. The following site includes many examples of this.

The Fibonacci Numbers in Nature
URL: http://www.mcs.surrey.ac.uk/Personal/R.Knott/Fibonacci/
   fibnat.html

Help students complete the spiral squares activity in Step B. Once they have drawn their figures and recorded the side lengths, have students open the following Web site.

The Fibonacci Rectangles and Shell Spirals
URL: http://www.mcs.surrey.ac.uk/Personal/R.Knott/Fibonacci/
   fibnat.html#Spiral

This page shows an animation of the spiral squares and connects this figure to one example of Fibonacci numbers in nature.

PATTERNS WITH NUMBERS

NAME:_____

DATE:_____

Step A

The following number pattern was first described by an Italian mathematician named Fibonacci. Continue the pattern.

1, 1, 2, 3, 5, 8, 13, 21, 34, ____, ____, ____, ____

Step B

Follow the instructions to illustrate the Fibonacci sequence.

Draw squares in a spiral around the one shown on page 53.

1. Begin by drawing a square on top of the one shown. Make sure the sides of the square are the same length as the top of the starting square.

2. Now draw a square to the left of your figure. The sides of this square should be the same length as the left side of your figure.

3. Continue drawing 4 more squares in a spiral. The next square should be drawn along the bottom of the figure, the next to the right, and so on.

Permission granted to photocopy for classroom use only. ©1998 Classroom Connect 1-(800) 638-1639 URL: http://www.classroom.com

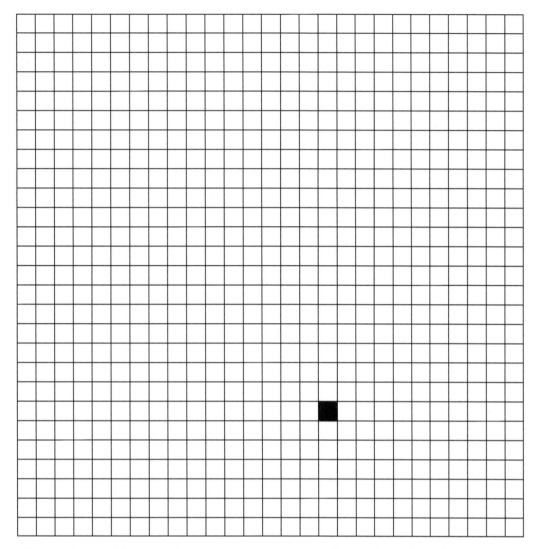

4. Record the side length of each square you drew. Explain what you notice about these lengths.

_____

5. Go to this Web site.

The Fibonacci Rectangles
URL: http://www.mcs.surrey.ac.uk/Personal/R.Knott/Fibonacci/
    fibnat.html#Spiral

Where in nature might you find the pattern you drew?

_____

_____

Permission granted to photocopy for classroom use only. ©1998 Classroom Connect 1-(800) 638-1639 URL: http://www.classroom.com

MULTIPLICATION MAGIC

Overview

To some students, the ability to multiply large numbers mentally seems like magic. In this lesson, students will learn a few mental math techniques.

Time Frame

One 45-minute session

Objectives

• Learn mental math techniques for multiplying 2-, 3-, and 4-digit numbers.

Materials

• Computer with Internet access
• SPECIAL BROWSER NEEDS: Java-capable Browser (Netscape 3.0+ or Explorer 3.0+)

Procedure

❶ Before starting the lesson, you may wish to review place value concepts and basic multiplication facts because many mental math procedures rely heavily on these skills. Discuss with students when the ability to multiply mentally might come in handy. Explain that in this lesson they will learn many techniques for multiplying large numbers with mental math.

Show students a series of problems such as the one below. Have them look for patterns and make any generalizations they can about multiplying by multiples of 10, 100, and 1,000.

$3 \times 6 = 18$

$3 \times 60 = 180$

$3 \times 600 = 1,800$

$30 \times 6,000 = 180,000$

Once they understand the place value and zero patterns evident in these problems, have them complete Step A of the Activity Sheet.

❸ Have students go to the following Web site to learn how to multiply any 2-digit number by 11.

Eleven Times
URL: http://www.LearningKingdom.com/eleven/eleven.html

Once students click to start, they must watch the animation closely as it runs automatically. Suggest that they view 2 or 3 examples before moving on to see what happens if the sum is a 2-digit number. Have them view 2 or 3 examples of this as well. When they are ready to test their skills, they can click *I'm ready for the Eleven Times Challenge* or go to the following Web page.

Eleven Times Challenge
URL: http://www.LearningKingdom.com/eleven/eleventest.html

❹ Another mental math technique involves breaking numbers apart into smaller numbers whose products can be added together. Show students the following examples to demonstrate this technique.

$602 \times 5 = ?$ $725 \times 4 = ?$

Think: $600 \times 5 = 3,000$ Think: $700 \times 4 = 2,800$

$2 \times 5 = 10$ $25 \times 4 = 100$

$3,000 + 10 = 3,010$ $2,800 + 100 = 2,900$

❺ If one of the numbers you are multiplying is close to a multiple of 10, 100, or 1,000, the product can be found with a little mental subtraction.

$19 \times 5 = ?$ $399 \times 4 = ?$

Think: $20 \times 5 = 100$ Think: $400 \times 4 = 1,600$

$100 - 5 = 95$ $1,600 - 4 = 1,596$

This example combines the techniques described above.

$729 \times 3 = ?$

Think: $700 \times 3 = 2,100$

$29 \times 3 = ?$ $30 \times 3 = 90$ $90 - 3 = 87$

$2,100 + 87 = 2,187$

Once students have seen a few examples of the techniques shown above, have them complete Step C.

MULTIPLICATION MAGIC

NAME: _____

DATE: _____

Step A

Find each product using mental math.

1. 3 × 600 = _____   2. 12 × 2,000 = _____   3. 40 × 70 = _____

4. 50 × 300 = _____   5. 900 × 20 = _____   6. 8,000 × 60 = _____

7. 400 × 800 = _____   8. 700 × 5,000 = _____   9. 10,000 × 90 = _____

Step B

Go to the following Web site to learn a mental math magic trick.

Eleven Times
URL: http://www.LearningKingdom.com/eleven/eleven.html

After you have gone through a few of the examples, try the Eleven Times Challenge.

Step C

Find each product using mental math.

1. 8 × 23 = _____   2. 315 × 4 = _____   3. 55 × 7 = _____

4. 9 × 204 = _____   5. 507 × 60 = _____   6. 29 × 3 = _____

Explain how you could use mental math to find each product.

7. 94 × 3

    _____

8. 7 × 49

    _____

Permission granted to photocopy for classroom use only. ©1998 Classroom Connect 1-(800) 638-1639 URL: http://www.classroom.com

MULTICULTURAL MULTIPLICATION

Overview

In this lesson, students will learn about Egyptian numbers and Egyptian methods for multiplying numbers. This method allows students to multiply large numbers by using simple computational skills such as basic multiplication facts and addition.

Time Frame

One 45-minute session

Objectives

- Learn about Egyptian numbers
- Learn about the Egyptian doubling method for multiplication.

Materials

- Computer with Internet access

Procedure

1 Have students go to the following Web site to learn how to write Egyptian numbers.

Egyptian Numbers
URL: http://eyelid.ukonline.co.uk/ancient/numbers.htm

Ask students to complete Step A of the Activity Sheet.

Groups of 6	Egyptian Number	Total
1	⦀⦀	6
2	∩ ‖	12
4	∩∩ ‖‖	24
8	∩∩∩∩ ‖‖‖‖	48

❷ The Egyptians used a doubling process to multiply numbers. A table of doubles was created by starting with a number and doubling each entry. By looking at how the Egyptians recorded numbers, it becomes clear that the doubling process required little more than duplicating symbols and regrouping when necessary.

To find the product of 14 × 6, think of the problem as finding the total of 14 groups of 6. Since 8 + 4 + 2 = 14, you can add 48 + 24 + 12 to find that 14 groups of 6 equals 84.

To learn more about Egyptian multiplication, see the section on Egyptian mathematics at the following Web site.

Babylonian and Egyptian Mathematics
URL: http://www-history.mcs.st-and.ac.uk/history/HistTopics/
        Babylonian_and_Egyptian.html

Activity
Sheet
15

MULTICULTURAL MULTIPLICATION

NAME: _____

DATE:_____

Step **A**

Go to this Web site to see how the Egyptians wrote numbers.

Egyptian Numbers
URL: http://eyelid.ukonline.co.uk/ancient/numbers.htm

Use Egyptian numbers to write each of these.

7 _____

11 _____

14 _____

17 _____

83 _____

102_____

357_____

Permission granted to photocopy for classroom use only. ©1998 Classroom Connect 1-(800) 638-1639 URL: http://www.classroom.com

Egyptians multiplied numbers by using a method called doubling. Here is how to find the product of 4 and 24.

- Write 24 using Egyptian numbers in the first row of the table.

- In the second row, double 24 by showing twice as many symbols as you did in the first row. Write the total in the last column.

- Finally, double the number in the second row and write the total. Remember the Egyptian number system was similar to ours. When you have 10 of one type of symbol, regroup them for the next larger symbol.

Groups of 24	Egyptian Number	Total
1		24
2		
4		

To find 3 × 24, use the information in the table and add groups of 24 together.

_____ + _____ = _____

1 group of 24   2 groups of 24   3 groups of 24

Use this method to find 6 × 24

_____ + _____ = _____

2 groups of 24   4 groups of 24   6 groups of 24

MULTICULTURAL MULTIPLICATION

Permission granted to photocopy for classroom use only. ©1998 Classroom Connect 1-(800) 638-1639 URL: http://www.classroom.com

ESTIMATING COSTS

Overview

In this lesson, students will practice estimating and finding sums of money while learning to choose healthy foods.

Time Frame

One 45-minute session

Objectives

• Practice finding sums of money amounts.
• Estimate sums of money to determine if there is enough.
• Learn about the 5 food groups.

Materials

• Computer with Internet access

Procedure

❶ Review how to find sums of money amounts. Remind students of the importance of lining up the decimal point and including the dollar sign when adding money. Have students complete items 1–8 on the Activity Sheet.

2 Discuss the usefulness of estimating money amounts when out on a shopping trip. Since you don't always have paper and pencil handy, estimation and mental math are helpful skills. Review the concept of rounding and discuss the advantages and disadvantages of overestimating and underestimating. Have students complete items 9–12 on the Activity Sheet.

3 Have students go to the following Web site.

The Food Guide Pyramid
URL: http://www.kidsfood.org/f_pyramid/pyramid.html

Have them record the information on the Food Guide Pyramid in the table on the Activity Sheet. Explain that they will be using this information in the Cyber Food Shopper Game.

Once students have completed their tables, have them go to the following Web site.

Cyber Food Shopper
URL: http://www.kidsfood.org/choices/shopper.html

Go over the game rules with students. Suggest that they use the space provided on the Activity Sheet to calculate totals and record the items they wish to put on their list before submitting their final list.

Extension

Have small groups put together a menu for the day. The foods they plan on eating should adhere to the Food Guide Pyramid suggestions. Provide students with a number of grocery ads from the newspaper. Have them create a shopping list for their menu. Remind students to buy enough for everyone in their group. For an extra challenge, ask groups to spend less than $50 each.

ESTIMATING COSTS

NAME: _____

DATE: _____

Step A

Find each sum.

1. $1.35
  + 2.65
	2. $3.41
	  + 5.09
		3. $2.71
		  + 0.89
			4. $4.56
			  + 1.14

5. $2.98
    1.42
  + 3.65
	6. $1.73
	    0.81
	  + 2.54
		7. $2.36
		    0.57
		  + 3.45
			8. $4.67
			    3.99
			  + 0.31

Suppose you have $5.00 to spend. Estimate the total cost and decide if you have enough money for both items.

	Item 1	Item 2	Estimated Cost for Both	Enough Money?
9.	Wheat Flakes $3.69	Milk $1.99		Yes No
10.	Orange Juice $2.29	Hash Browns $2.49		Yes No
11.	Roast Beef $3.99	French Bread $1.29		Yes No
12.	Chicken $3.49	Tomatoes $0.99		Yes No

Permission granted to photocopy for classroom use only. ©1998 Classroom Connect 1-(800) 638-1639 URL: http://www.classroom.com

Use the Food Guide Pyramid at this Web site to complete the table.

The Food Guide Pyramid
URL: http://www.kidsfood.org/f_pyramid/pyramid.html

Name of Food Group	Number of Servings per Day

Go to the following Web site and play the Cyber Food Shopper Game!

Cyber Food Shopper Game
URL: http://www.kidsfood.org/choices/shopper.html

Use the space below to plan which foods you will buy.

Record the items you will submit for your shopping list.

My Shopping List		
Supermarket	Farmers' Market	Corner Store

Permission granted to photocopy for classroom use only. ©1998 Classroom Connect 1-(800) 638-1639 URL: http://www.classroom.com

THE IDITAROD DOG SLED RACE

 ## Overview

In this lesson, students will apply math skills such as subtracting, calculating rates, and converting units of time to solve real-world problems related to the Iditarod Dog Sled Race. They will use data from previous races to plan their own racing strategies.

 ## Time Frame

Two 45-minute sessions

 ## Objectives

• Apply math skills to real-world problems.
• Learn about the Iditarod Dog Sled Race.

 ## Materials

• Computer with Internet access
• OPTIONAL: calculator

 ## Procedure

1 Before starting the lesson, you may wish to review procedures for converting between units of time as well as for calculating rates such as miles per hour. Organize students into pairs or groups if desired. Make sure each student or group has a copy of the instructions on the Activity Sheet. Have them begin this activity by reading the history and background of the Iditarod Dog Sled Race at the following Web site.

Iditarod Dog Sled Race: History and Background
URL: http://www.pbs.org/learn/mathline/concepts/feb98/
    conceptshistory.html

When students are ready to begin the first activity, have them click *Activity 1: Checkpoints* from the menu at the left of the page or type in the following address into their browser.

Activity 1: Checkpoints
URL: http://www.pbs.org/learn/mathline/concepts/feb98/
    conceptsactivity1.html

Have students print out the page or use a separate piece of paper to record their answers. Printing the Checkpoint Table is recommended.

Help students understand how each entry in the Checkpoint Table is calculated. In Part II of the activity, the 1997 winning time is given in days, hours, minutes, and seconds. Help students convert the time into hours for simpler calculation of the rate. Encourage students to estimate. You may wish to provide access to calculators.

Once students or groups have decided on a reasonable rate, have them complete the Race Log on the Activity Sheet.

❷ Have students click *Activity 2: Winning Times* from the menu or type in the following address into their browser.

Activity 2: Winning Times
URL: http://www.pbs.org/learn/mathline/concepts/feb98/
    conceptsactivity2.html

Make sure students record their answers to each question. Help students convert all winning times to hours as this will help them when calculating rates in miles per hour.

Once students have completed this activity, have them click *Activity 3: Huskies* from the menu or use the following address.

Activity 3: Huskies
URL: http://www.pbs.org/learn/mathline/concepts/feb98/
    conceptsactivity3.html

Again, students should record their answers. Have students share their answers to question 3 and discuss why they would or wouldn't place the same amount of dog food at each checkpoint.

THE IDITAROD DOG SLED RACE

NAME:_____

DATE:_____

1. Go to this Web site to read about the Iditarod Dog Sled Race.

   Iditarod Dog Sled Race: History and Background
   URL: http://www.pbs.org/learn/mathline/concepts/feb98/
         conceptshistory.html

2. When you're ready for the first activity, click *Activity 1: Checkpoints* from the menu. Print the page or use a separate piece of paper to record your answers. Use the rate you choose for question 6 to complete your Race Log.

Race Log		
Checkpoints	Distance Between Checkpoints	Estimated Time
Eagle River		
Wasilla		
Knik		
Yentna		
Skwentna		
Finger Lake		
Rainy Pass		
Rohn		
Nikolai		
McGrath		
Takotna		
Ophir		
Cripple		
Ruby		
Galena		
Nulato		
Kaltag		
Unalakleet		
Shaktoolik		
Koyuk		
Elim		
Golovin		
White Mountain		
Safety		
Nome		

Permission granted to photocopy for classroom use only. ©1998 Classroom Connect   1-(800) 638-1639   URL: http://www.classroom.com

3. To move on, click *Activity 2: Winning Times* from the menu. Read each question carefully to be sure you convert times to the correct units. Remember to record your answers.

_____

_____

_____

_____

_____

_____

_____

4. Take care of your dogs! Click *Activity 3: Huskies* to plan out your dogs' food supply for the race. Discuss your answers with the class.

_____

_____

_____

_____

_____

_____

_____

_____

Permission granted to photocopy for classroom use only. ©1998 Classroom Connect   1-(800) 638-1639   URL: http://www.classroom.com

ATHLETES AVERAGES

Overview

Averages such as the median and the mean can be useful ways of describing an athlete's performance. But what happens to players' career averages if they get hurt and don't play for a good part of the season? In this lesson, students will practice finding the median and the mean of data sets. They will learn about outliers and explore how outliers affect the median and the mean of a data set.

Time Frame

One 45-minute session

Objectives

- Review finding the median and the mean of a data set.
- Learn about outliers in a data set.
- Explore the effect of outliers on the median and the mean.

Materials

- Computer with Internet access
- OPTIONAL: Calculator

 # Procedure

1 Discuss different uses of the word "average" with the class. Explain that when dealing with statistics, *average* often refers to the mean but it can refer to any measure of central tendency. Review the median as the middle value of an ordered data set and the mean as the sum of all data divided by the number of values.

2 Hank Aaron played Major League Baseball for 23 seasons from 1954–1976. He is best known for holding the career record of 755 home runs. Have students practice finding the median and the mean number of home runs Aaron hit in a season. Students may need help finding the home run column ("HR") in the table at the following Web site.

Hank Aaron's Career Statistics
URL: http://www.cwws.net/~schubert/stats.htm

Here is an ordered list of Aaron's 23 seasons that you may want to share with students.
10, 12, 13, 20, 24, 26, 27, 29, 30, 32, 34, 34, 38, 39, 39, 40, 40, 44, 44, 44, 44, 45, 47

Have students complete Step A of the Activity Sheet.

3 Introduce the term "outlier" to the class. Explain that an outlier is a piece of data that is either extremely high or extremely low in comparison to all other data.

Jerry Rice is one of the leading receivers in professional football. Have students go to the following Web site to find Jerry Rice's career statistics.

Jerry Rice's Career Statistics
URL: http://cnnsi.com/football/nfl/players/Jerry.Rice/#Career

Have students use the Receptions column ("Rec.") of the Receiving table to answer the first question in Step B of the Activity Sheet. Notice that the number of receptions in 1997 is considerably lower than the number of receptions for all other seasons. An injury to Rice's knee kept him from playing 14 out of 16 games that season. Help students complete Step B. Talk about some of the students' responses. Explain that outliers affect the mean more than the median.

4 Have students complete a similar activity in Step C.

ATHLETES AVERAGES

NAME:_____

DATE:_____

Step   A

Go to the following Web site to find the number of home runs Hank Aaron hit in each season of his career.

Hank Aaron's Career Statistics
URL: http://www.cwws.net/~schubert/stats.htm

1. Find the median and the mean of this data.

   Median = _____

   Mean = _____

2. Both the median and the mean tell about how many home runs Hank Aaron hit in a season. Which do you think is a better description of the data? Explain.

   _____

   _____

Step   B

Jerry Rice is one of the leading receivers in professional football. Go to the following Web site to see the number of receptions ("Rec.") Jerry Rice has made in his career.

Jerry Rice's Career Statistics
URL: http://cnnsi.com/football/nfl/players/Jerry.Rice/#Career

1. What is the outlier in this data set? How do you know?

   _____

   _____

Permission granted to photocopy for classroom use only. ©1998 Classroom Connect 1-(800) 638-1639 URL: http://www.classroom.com

2. Find the median and the mean of the data with and without the outlier.

Average Number of Receptions in a Season

	Using Data from All Seasons Played	Using Data Without Outlier(s)
Median		
Mean		

3. Calculate the difference between the median values as well as the mean values you found. What effect did the outlier have on the mean? The median?

_____

_____

4. Is the median or the mean is a better description of the data? Why?

_____

_____

| Step | C |

Michael Jordan is one of the highest scoring players in the NBA. Find the total points Jordan scored in each season of his career at this Web site.

Michael Jordan's Career Statistics
URL: http://cnnsi.com/basketball/nba/players/Michael.Jordan/#Career Stats

(Hint: For total points, use the next-to-last column of the bottom table!)

1. List any outliers you find for this data set.

_____

2. Complete the table to find out about how many points Jordan scores in a season.

Average Number of Points Scored in a Season

	Using Data from All Seasons Played	Using Data Without Outlier(s)
Median		
Mean		

3. Do you think the median or the mean is a better description of Michael Jordan's career performance? Explain.

_____

Permission granted to photocopy for classroom use only. ©1998 Classroom Connect 1-(800) 638-1639 URL: http://www.classroom.com

SNOWFLAKE GEOMETRY

Overview

Geometric concepts and terms were developed to help people describe the world around them. In this lesson, students will review how to draw and measure angles and will explore the concept of symmetry. They will use these concepts to make paper snowflakes and to identify shapes and symmetry in their snowflakes.

Time Frame

One 45-minute session

Objectives

- Measure and draw angles.
- Identify and describe shapes.
- Identify lines of symmetry.

Materials

- Computer with Internet access
- Protractor
- Ruler
- Scissors

Procedure

1 Demonstrate how to use a protractor to measure and draw angles. Explain the following types of angles and show some examples.

Acute - An angle measuring less than 90°
Right - A 90° angle
Obtuse - An angle measuring more than 90°
Straight - A 180° angle

Have students practice measuring, drawing, and classifying angles.

2 Describe line symmetry to students. Illustrate the following shapes and discuss lines of symmetry for each.

Square - 4 lines of symmetry
Isosceles Triangle - 1 line of symmetry
Parallelogram - No lines of symmetry

Students who have difficulty with this concept may benefit by cutting and folding a shape to check for line symmetry.

3 Have students go to the following Web site to make a paper snowflake.

Snowflakes You Can Make
URL: http://members.surfsouth.com/~rlogue/snowup.htm

Students can cut out the square on the Activity Sheet to begin their snowflakes. Once students have followed the online instructions to complete their snowflakes, have them answer the questions in Step B of the Activity Sheet.

SNOWFLAKE GEOMETRY

NAME:_____

DATE:_____

Step   A

Go to this Web site and follow the instructions to make a paper snowflake.

Snowflakes You Can Make
URL: http://members.surfsouth.com/~rlogue/snowup.htm

You can cut out the square below to begin your snowflake.

1. List all of the shapes you can find in your snowflake. Explain how you know what type of shapes they are.

   _____

   _____

   _____

   _____

2. Use your ruler to draw all lines of symmetry on the back of your snowflake. How many lines of symmetry does your snowflake have?

   _____

   _____

   _____

   _____

3. Are all of the folds in your snowflake lines of symmetry? Explain.

   _____

   _____

   _____

   _____

4. Compare your snowflake to one of your classmates' snowflakes. Describe how they are alike and how they are different.

   _____

   _____

   _____

   _____

Permission granted to photocopy for classroom use only. ©1998 Classroom Connect   1-(800) 638-1639   URL: http://www.classroom.com

PATTERNS AND TESSELLATIONS

Overview

In this lesson, students will connect geometric concepts such as slides, flips, and turns to artistic patterns. They will explore tessellations by creating their own patterns with figures.

Time Frame

One 45-minute session

Objectives

- Review concepts of motion geometry: slides, flips, and turns.
- Explore and create patterns using slides, flips, and turns.
- Learn about and create tessellations.

Materials

- Computer with Internet access
- Scissors
- Tape
- Paper (or tag board if available)
- OPTIONAL: Colored pencils or markers

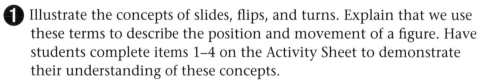

Procedure

1 Illustrate the concepts of slides, flips, and turns. Explain that we use these terms to describe the position and movement of a figure. Have students complete items 1–4 on the Activity Sheet to demonstrate their understanding of these concepts.

Many interesting and beautiful patterns can be created with the same figure just by using these motions. Have students choose one of the figures on the Activity Sheet or draw one of their own. Students should trace and cut out their figures and use slides, flips, and turns to create a pattern. Discuss what movements were used to create the patterns.

2 Explain that a tessellation is a special kind of repeating pattern that covers a surface leaving no empty spaces. The figures in a tessellation do not overlap. Go to the following Web site to learn more about tessellations and the mathematics behind them.

What Is a Tessellation?
URL: http://forum.swarthmore.edu/sum95/suzanne/whattess.html

Find out if any of the students happened to create a tessellation in the first activity. Have them discuss why their patterns are or are not tessellations.

3 Have students go to the following Web site to learn how to create a figure that tessellates. You may visit this site by typing the address below into your browser or by clicking the link on the Teaching Mathematics with the Internet Web page.

Steps to Create a Tessellating Shape
URL: http://www.inform.umd.edu:8080/UMS+State/UMD-Projects/
    MCTP/Technology/School_WWW_Pages/Tessellations/
    1996Project/HowWeDidIt.html

Each student will need to start with a square piece of paper or heavy tag board. Relate the movement of each cutout to the concept of slides presented earlier. Once students have created their figures, have them trace their figure repeatedly in the space provided to create a tessellation.

Extensions

Go to the following Web site to see tessellations created by other students.

Student Tessellations
URL: http://forum.swarthmore.edu/alejandre/students.tess.html

Discuss the use of tessellations in art. You may wish to introduce students to the artist M.C. Escher. Information about the artist can be found at the following Web sites.

M.C. Escher's Life
URL: http://library.advanced.org/11750/escherlife.shtml

M.C. Escher Collection
URL: http://gauss.technion.ac.il/~rl/M.C.Escher/

Activity
Sheet
20

PATTERNS AND TESSELLATIONS

NAME:_____

DATE:_____

Write *slide, flip,* or *turn* to describe each picture.

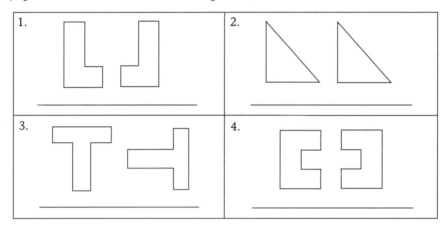

1.	2.
3.	4.

Choose one of the figures below or think of your own. Trace and cut out your figure. Use it to create a pattern using slides, flips, and turns.

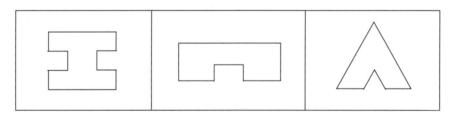

Permission granted to photocopy for classroom use only. ©1998 Classroom Connect   1-(800) 638-1639   URL: http://www.classroom.com

Are there any empty spaces in the pattern you created? A special kind of pattern that doesn't leave any empty spaces between figures is called a tessellation.

Go to this Web site to learn how to make a figure that tessellates. Then use your figure to create a tessellation below.

Steps to Create a Tessellating Shape
URL: http://www.inform.umd.edu:8080/UMS+State/UMD-Projects/
        MCTP/Technology/School_WWW_Pages/Tessellations/
        1996Project/HowWeDidIt.html

Permission granted to photocopy for classroom use only. ©1998 Classroom Connect 1-(800) 638-1639 URL: http://www.classroom.com

ISLAMIC PATTERNS

Overview

In this lesson, students will learn about circles and parts of circles. They will construct circles with a compass. To explore circles in art, they will create an Islamic pattern.

Time Frame

One 45-minute session

Objectives

- Learn vocabulary related to circles.
- Construct circles using a compass.
- Create patterns with circles.

Materials

- Computer with Internet access
- Compass
- Ruler
- OPTIONAL: Colored pencils or markers

 # Procedure

1 Introduce the following vocabulary related to circles.

Circle   A closed curve made up of points that are all the same distance from the center.

Radius   A line from the center to any point on the circle.

Diameter   A line from one point on the circle to another that passes through the center.

Chord   A line from one point on the circle to another that doesn't pass through the center.

Have students complete the table in Step A of the Activity Sheet.

2 Demonstrate how to use a compass. If students' compasses don't show the radius, show students how to use a ruler to create a circle with a specific radius. Have students use a compasss to complete Step A.

3 Introduce the use of geometric forms in Islamic art. For information on Islamic patterns, go to the following Web sites.

Geometry and Islam
URL: http://www.askasia.org/frclasrm/lessplan/1000030.htm

The Art of Oriental Carpets
URL: http://forum.swarthmore.edu/geometry/rugs/

Have students follow the instructions at the following Web site to complete Step B of the Activity Sheet.

Islamic Pattern Project
URL: http://www.askasia.org/image/drawing/i000531a.htm

Although the actual measure of the circle need not be exact, suggest that students keep the radius under 1.5 inches. If they would rather draw larger circles, they will want to use a larger piece of paper. Help them find the hexagonal star in their drawing. Students may opt to color their designs.

ISLAMIC PATTERNS

NAME: _____

DATE: _____

1. Use the circle to complete the table.

Part of the Circle	Label
radius	
	BE
	CD
center point	

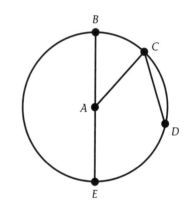

Use a compass and a ruler to draw each circle.

2.   Radius = 1 inch
     Center labeled $\overline{A}$
     Chord: $\overline{BC}$

3.   Diameter = 3 inches
     Center labeled $\overline{X}$
     Radius: $\overline{XY}$

4.   Diameter = 1 inch
     Radius: $\overline{PQ}$
     Chord: $\overline{QR}$

5.   Radius: $\overline{GH}$
     Chord: $\overline{HI}$
     Diameter: $\overline{JK}$

Permission granted to photocopy for classroom use only. ©1998 Classroom Connect   1-(800) 638-1639   URL: http://www.classroom.com

Islamic artists used geometric patterns to decorate everything from books and pots to rugs and walls. A common geometric shape used in Islamic art is the hexagonal star. Go to the following Web site and follow the instructions to create an Islamic design.

Islamic Pattern Project
URL: http://www.askasia.org/image/drawing/i000531a.htm

See if you can find a hexagonal star in your design!

Permission granted to photocopy for classroom use only. ©1998 Classroom Connect   1-(800) 638-1639   URL: http://www.classroom.com

TANGRAM MATH

Overview

Historians speculate that tangrams were invented in China about 250 years ago. The pieces in a tangram puzzle are useful for exploring a number of mathematical concepts. In this lesson, students will construct a set of tangrams and use it to explore concepts of fractions and area.

Time Frame

One 45-minute session

Objectives

• Explore fractional relationships among shapes.
• Connect fractional relationships among shapes to the concept of area.

Materials

• Computer with Internet access
• Paper
• Scissors

Procedure

1 Begin the lesson by having students go to the following Web site to make their own set of tangrams.

Tangram Construction
URL: http://forum.swarthmore.edu/trscavo/tangrams/construct.html

Have them explore the tangram pieces by putting them together to form a square. One solution to this puzzle can be found at the top of the Tangram Construction page.

2 Go to the following Web site and read through the activity.

Tangrams and Fractions
URL: http://forum.swarthmore.edu/paths/fractions/frac.tangram.html

Begin by having students think of the large square that they made as one whole. In Step B of the Activity Sheet, have students write the fractional part that each type of tangram piece represents.

Some students may benefit by tracing the perimeter of their square before moving pieces around. Demonstrate how pieces can be moved and stacked to compare size.

Help students see that pieces such as the small square and the parallelogram can be made up of 2 small triangles. Challenge them to write the fraction in simplest form.

Discuss that the same piece can represent different fractional parts depending on the definition of the whole. Have students write the fraction each piece represents if the large triangle equals one whole.

3 Introduce the concept of area as the number of square units needed to cover a figure. The following Web site contains an activity in which students find the area of each tangram piece without the use of formulas.

Areas of Tangram Pieces
URL: http://forum.swarthmore.edu/trscavo/tangrams/area.html

Have students use the fractional relationships they discovered in Step B to help them determine the areas of each tangram piece. Have them think of the small square as 1 square unit. Have students complete Step C of the Activity Sheet.

Extensions

1 For students interested in attempting to rearrange their tangram pieces into other figures, go to the following Web site for tangram puzzles. Students can click links on the page to find more tangram puzzles.

Tangram Puzzles - Set 1
URL: http://www.ex.ac.uk/cimt/puzzles/tangrams/tangset1.htm

2 Have students create their own designs and pictures with their tangrams. They can draw pictures of their creations and trade them with classmates. Suggest that each design include all seven pieces.

TANGRAM MATH

NAME:_____

DATE:_____

Step A

The exact origin of the tangram puzzle is unknown. However, it is thought to have been invented about 250 years ago in China. Go to the following Web site to make your own set of tangrams.

Tangram Construction
URL: http://forum.swarthmore.edu/trscavo/tangrams/construct.html

Once you've made your pieces, rearrange them to make a square. Draw a sketch here to show how you did it.

Permission granted to photocopy for classroom use only. ©1998 Classroom Connect   1-(800) 638-1639   URL: http://www.classroom.com

Think of the large square that you made as one whole. Write the fraction each tangram piece shows.

1.   Large triangle = _____

2.   Medium triangle = _____

3.   Small triangle = _____

4.   Small square = _____

5.   Parallelogram = _____

Write the fraction each tangram piece shows if the large triangular piece is one whole.

6.   Medium triangle = _____

7.   Small triangle = _____

8.   Small square = _____

9.   Parallelogram = _____

Step **C**

If the small square equals 1 square unit, find the areas of the other tangram shapes.

1.   Small triangle = _____ square unit(s)

2.   Medium triangle = _____ square unit(s)

3.   Large triangle = _____ square unit(s)

4.   Parallelogram = _____ square unit(s)

Permission granted to photocopy for classroom use only. ©1998 Classroom Connect   1-(800) 638-1639   URL: http://www.classroom.com

TRAVEL PLANS

Overview

In this lesson, students will take a tour of the United States in a Cessna airplane. They will use various math skills such as identifying fractional parts as well as estimating sums to solve real-world problems along the way. Students will then work in groups to plan their own trip with a given budget and time frame.

Time Frame

Two or three 45-minute sessions

Objectives

• Apply math skills to solving real-world problems.
• Work in teams to solve problems.

Materials

• Computer with Internet access

Procedure

1 Have students click *Go On* on the following Web page to begin the activity.

Plane Math: Fill 'Er Up
URL: http://www.planemath.com/activities/fillup/fillup1.html

Help students complete the activity. Review skills as necessary. To see a list of prerequisite skills, visit the teacher page for this activity at the following Web site.

TEACHING MATHEMATICS WITH THE INTERNET

Fill 'Er Up: Teacher Notes
URL: http://www.planemath.com/activities/fillup/fillupteachers.html

❷ Organize students into groups of 3–4. Explain that they are to work together to plan a one-week trip that costs no more than $1,000. They will be using resources found on the Internet to help. Each group will decide where it will go and how it will get there. Remind them to include costs for all group members. Discuss some of the types of expenses they had in the online activity. Explain that each group will have the chance to present their travel plans to the class. Before they begin, be sure to describe all of the information you expect to see in their presentations. Here are some questions you might ask students to answer.

- Where are you going?
- How will you get there?
- How much will it cost for your group to get there?
- What type(s) of transportation will you use once you're there? How much will it cost?
- Where will you spend each night? How much will it cost to stay there?
- What points of interest will you visit there? Are there any admission fees or costs for these places?
- How much will you budget for food each day? What do you plan on eating?

⭐Extension

Go to the following page to explore the collection of other activities available at the Plane Math web site. All of the activities have students apply math skills to solving real-world problems. Check the teacher notes page of any of the activities to view a brief summary of the lesson objectives.

Plane Math Activities
URL: http://www.planemath.com/activities/pmactivitiesall.html

One example is the Flight Path activity. Students use visual estimation as well as estimation of sums to find the shortest path from San Francisco to New York.

Plane Math: Flight Path
URL: http://www.planemath.com/activities/flightpath/flightpathhome.html

TRAVEL PLANS

NAME: _____

DATE: _____

How would you like to fly a plane around the United States? Go to this Web site and click *Go On* to get going.

Plane Math: Fill 'Er Up
URL: http://www.planemath.com/activities/fillup/fillup1.html

Work with your group to plan a one-week trip that costs no more than $1,000. You may use any of the Web sites below to help you plan your trip.

Distance Finder
URL: http://www.indo.com/distance/

Yahoo! Book a Flight
URL: http://travel.yahoo.com/destinations/travelocity_air/
        yfinal_flts_roundtrip.html

Greyhound Fares and Schedules
URL: http://www.greyhound.com/Fares/fares.html

Yahoo! Book a Car Rental
URL: http://travel.yahoo.com/destinations/travelocity_car/yfinal_car.html

Yahoo! Book a Hotel Room
URL: http://travel.yahoo.com/destinations/travelocity_hotel/yfinal_hotel.html

Permission granted to photocopy for classroom use only. ©1998 Classroom Connect 1-(800) 638-1639 URL: http://www.classroom.com

Present your group's travel plans to the rest of the class. You can record your plans and your expense budget below. Write other notes about your trip on this page as well.

Itinerary

Sunday	Monday	Tuesday	Wednesday	Thursday	Friday	Saturday

Expenses

Transportation	Food	Entertainment	Lodging	Souvenirs/Other

Other Information

Permission granted to photocopy for classroom use only. ©1998 Classroom Connect 1-(800) 638-1639 URL: http://www.classroom.com

FRACTIONS AND FOOD

Overview

In this lesson, students will review fraction operations while planning meals for the class.

Time Frame

One 45-minute session

Objectives

- Review fraction operations.
- Apply math skills to solving real-world problems.
- Work in teams to solve problems.

Materials

- Computer with Internet access

Procedure

1 Review writing fractions and improper fractions in simplest form. A fraction is in simplest form if the greatest common factor of the numerator and the denominator equals 1. Demonstrate the process by showing an example such as 6/15. Create an ordered list of factors for both the numerator and the denominator.

6: 1, 2, 3, 6
15: 1, 3, 5, 15

Identify 3 as the greatest common factor and divide both the numerator and the denominator by it. The simplest form of 6/15 is 2/5.

2 Introduce the idea of doubling or tripling recipes in order to serve more people. Help students complete the chart in Step A of the Activity Sheet. Have them use their completed charts to decide how many batches they should make for each of the given scenarios. Discuss what they should do if making more batches creates more servings than they need.

3 Organize students into groups of 3 or 4. Explain that in Step B, each group will choose at least 2 recipes and adjust them to make enough food for the entire class. Determine the total number of people in the class and assign each group one of the following categories.
- Breakfast
- Lunch
- Dinner
- Dessert
- Appetizers
- Bread
- Side Dishes
- Soup
- Salad

Have students write their recipes on their Activity Sheets. Groups should be prepared to present their recipes and explain how they adjusted the original recipes.

Extensions

1 Have each group prepare a cookbook page for their recipes. Collect the recipes and create a class cookbook. If possible have students plan a meal using the cookbook. Help them shop for all the supplies they need and prepare a feast for the class.

2 Go to the following Web site for an extended project idea. Although it is suggested that the project run over 10 days, you could tailor the project to your time and interests.

Fine Dining
URL: http://www.nsa.gov:8080/programs/mepp/es/frac02.html

FRACTIONS AND FOOD

NAME:_____

DATE:_____

Step   **A**

Have you ever cooked for a large group? Most recipes are written to serve less than 10 people. If you want to prepare a meal for a large group, you will probably need to adjust the recipe.

1. The chart below shows the number of servings you can make if you cook more than one batch of the original recipe. Complete the chart and use it to answer the questions below.

Number of Batches	Original recipe serves...				
	4 people	5 people	6 people	7 people	8 people
2	8				
3		15		21	24
4					
5			30		
6	24				

Write the number of batches you should make for each.

2. The original recipe serves 7. You want to cook enough for 28 people.

   _____

3. The original recipe serves 8. You want to cook enough for 32 people.

   _____

4. The original recipe serves 8. You want to cook enough for 30 people.

   _____

5. The original recipe serves 6. You want to cook enough for 27 people.

   _____

Permission granted to photocopy for classroom use only. ©1998 Classroom Connect   1-(800) 638-1639   URL: http://www.classroom.com

Plan a meal for your class. Work with your group to find at least 2 recipes from one of the following categories: breakfast, lunch, dinner, dessert, appetizers, bread, side dishes, soup, or salad.

Go to the following Web sites to find recipes for foods your class would like to eat.

Dole Fruit and Vegetable Cookbook for Kids
URL: http://www.dole5aday.com/COOK/COOKBOOK.html

Kraft Cookbook
URL: http://www.kraftfoods.com/html/main/recbox.html

Adjust the recipes to feed everyone in your class and write them below. Be prepared to present your recipes to the class and explain how you adjusted the original recipe.

Permission granted to photocopy for classroom use only. ©1998 Classroom Connect 1-(800) 638-1639 URL: http://www.classroom.com

MEASURABLE IMPROVEMENTS

Overview

In this lesson, students will apply math skills such as calculating perimeter, reading scale drawings, and adding decimals to the real-world problems of home improvement planning. Given a house plan, students will work in small groups to determine how much paint, wallpaper, carpet, and tile they need for their home.

Time Frame

Two 45-minute sessions

Objectives

- Apply math skills to solving real-world problems.
- Work in teams to solve problems.

Materials

- Computer with Internet access

Procedure

1 You may want to begin by reviewing the concept of perimeter as the distance around a figure. Explain that in this lesson students will be given the dimensions of a room in feet and inches and will be asked to find the perimeter of the room. You may wish to review how to add measurements in feet and inches, as students will be required to regroup inches to feet.

Organize students into groups of 3 or 4. Have them go to the following Web site to select a house plan they want to use for the activity.

Alternative Home Plans
URL: http://www.alternativehomeplans.com/

Explain that groups will decide what improvements they want to make to their homes. All houses have at least one room that needs new paint. Groups can also choose from the following projects.

• New wallpaper
• New carpet
• New tile

3️⃣ While students are looking at their house plans, discuss the way that dimensions are recorded on the plans. For example, the notation 18 - 5 means 18 feet, 5 inches. Have them look for other special markings like window and door openings. Explain that house plans help people get a general idea about the layout of a home. The plans builders use to construct houses would include more information. One piece of information that is missing from the plans that students will be working with is wall (or ceiling) height. Explain that walls are generally between 8 and 10 feet high. Vaulted ceilings can be much higher. Each group should decide on reasonable wall heights for the rooms in their homes.

4️⃣ Help students fill in the table on page 100 of the Activity Sheet. When describing rooms, they may wish to number the bedrooms so that they know which dimensions to use. Guide them through the use of the other online calculators using information from their house plans.

5️⃣ Each group should write a report describing each home improvement project. The report should include a description of the house and what the group plans to change. It should list the materials needed for each project and an explanation of how the group determined each amount. Reports should include a discussion about overestimating and underestimating when dealing with materials needed for a project.

MEASURABLE IMPROVEMENTS

NAME:_____

DATE:_____

Go with your group to the following Web site and choose a house plan. This is will be your house.

Alternative Home Plans
URL: http://www.alternativehomeplans.com/

Once you have chosen a home, discuss with your teammates what you want to change in your home. All homes have at least one room that needs to be painted. Here are some other home improvement projects for your group to consider.

• New wallpaper for your bedroom, kitchen, or bathroom
• New carpet
• New tile for your kitchen or bathroom

Use your house plan to fill in the table below for each room that you want to paint. Wall heights are generally between 8 and 10 feet. Since many house plans don't include this dimension, your group can decide on the height of your walls. Use the Paint Calculator at the following Web site to find out how many gallons of paint you will need.

Paint Calculator
URL: http://www.bhglive.com/homeimp/docs/paintcal.htm

Room	Perimeter (in feet & inches)	Ceiling Height (between 8-10 feet)	Number of Single Doors	Number of Double Doors	Number of Small Windows	Number of Large Windows	Gallons of Paint Needed
						Total Gallons of Paint	

Permission granted to photocopy for classroom use only. ©1998 Classroom Connect 1-(800) 638-1639 URL: http://www.classroom.com

Fill out the forms at the following Web sites to help you plan your other projects. Some will ask for the dimensions of the room in feet instead of feet and inches. Remember that you are getting an idea about how much material you will need. Think about whether you should under-estimate or overestimate.

Wallpaper Calculator
URL: http://www.chase-pitkin.com/cgi-bin/chase-pitkin/
     displaycalc.cgi?choice=wallpaper

Carpet Calculator
URL: http://www.chase-pitkin.com/cgi-bin/chase-pitkin/
     displaycalc.cgi?choice=carpeting

Floor Tile Calculator
URL: http://www.homeideas.com/applets/tiles.asp

Write a report describing your home improvement projects. Include a description of the house and what you plan to change. List materials you will need and explain how your group came up with each amount. Discuss whether you overestimated or underestimated and why.

_____

_____

_____

_____

_____

_____

_____

_____

_____

_____

Permission granted to photocopy for classroom use only. ©1998 Classroom Connect 1-(800) 638-1639 URL: http://www.classroom.com

ALLOWABLE PERCENTS

Overview

In this lesson, students will connect percents to fractions and decimals. They will also apply their understanding of these connections to estimating percents.

Time Frame

One 45-minute session

Objectives

• Introduce the concept of percents.
• Connect fractions, decimals, and percents.
• Estimate amounts using benchmark percents.

Materials

• Computer with Internet access
• SPECIAL BROWSER NEEDS: Java-capable Browser (Netscape 3.0+ or Explorer 3.0+)
• Shockwave plug-in
  URL: http://www.macromedia.com/shockwave/download

# Procedure

1 Review connections between fractions and decimals. Explain that fractions and decimals are two different number systems that can be used to represent the same amounts. Introduce the concept of percents as another way of showing the same part-to-whole relationships. Explain that percent means "per 100, out of 100, or hundredth." Discuss where students have heard percentages used around them.

2 Have students go to the following Web site to test their estimation skills.

Face the Music
URL: http://www.theatrix.com/fun/games/ftm/ftm.html

3 To practice interpreting data and building estimation skills, have students go to the following Web site to access data about kids' allowances. Have them follow the instructions on page 105 of the Activity Sheet.

Kids' Money: Allowance Statistics
URL: http://pages.prodigy.com/kidsmoney/allstats.htm

Extension

If students are familiar with the method of finding the percent of a number by converting to a decimal and multiplying, they can go to the Allowance Statistics Web site and answer questions such as these.

WHEN TO BEGIN?
- According to the Global/Decima poll, how many parents felt five-year olds are too young to receive allowance?

TIED TO CHORES?
- According to CIBC, how many people thought kids should receive allowances for chores and good behavior?
- According to the Global/Decima poll, how many parents felt their kids needed to earn their allowances?

HOW MANY RECEIVE?
- According to Zillions magazine, how many kids surveyed receive an allowance?

ALLOWABLE PERCENTS

NAME:_____

DATE:_____

Practice estimating percent amounts by going to this Web site and playing *Face the Music*.

Face the Music
URL: http://www.theatrix.com/fun/games/ftm/ftm.html

Record your results below.

_____

_____

_____

_____

_____

_____

_____

_____

_____

_____

_____

Permission granted to photocopy for classroom use only. ©1998 Classroom Connect   1-(800) 638-1639   URL: http://www.classroom.com

The following Web site has lots of data about kids and the allowance they receive. Use this information to answer each question below.

Kids' Money: Allowance Statistics
URL: http://pages.prodigy.com/kidsmoney/allstats.htm

Click *Tied to Chores?* Find the results of each survey and write a fraction that tells about how many kids to do chores for their allowances.

1. May 1993 Liberty Survey

_____

2. Sixth Grade Survey

_____

Go back to the contents menu and click *How Many Receive?*

3. According to the May 1993 Liberty Survey, about what fraction of 8th graders receive allowances?

_____

_____

4. According to the Global/Decima poll, what fraction of the parents surveyed thought kids shouldn't receive allowances at any age?

_____

_____

Go back to the contents menu and click *Save a Portion?*

5. According to the 1993 Liberty Survey, what fraction of 10th graders save a portion of their allowance? About what fraction of 12th graders do?

_____

_____

6. According to the Sixth Grade Survey, about what fraction of 6th graders save a portion of their allowance?

_____

_____

Permission granted to photocopy for classroom use only. ©1998 Classroom Connect 1-(800) 638-1639 URL: http://www.classroom.com

100% M&M s

Overview

In this lesson, students will interpret circle graphs using data about M&M's color combinations. Students will also find percentages of a number. Depending on students' prior knowledge, they can either do this by converting the percent into a decimal and multiplying or they can solve proportions.

Time Frame

One 45-minute session

Objectives

- Interpret circle graphs.
- Calculate percentages.

Materials

- Computer with Internet access
- RealAudio plug in (optional)
  URL: http://www.realaudio.com

Procedure

1 Have students go to the following Web site and click *Color Combinations* to view the official color distribution percentages of M&M's candies.

M&M/Mars
URL: http://www.m-ms.com/faq/

You may wish to discuss the similarities and differences between the different types of M&M's. Have students refer to the plain M&M's data for this activity. Help students complete items 1–5 of Step A on the Activity Sheet. Explain that it is not a coincidence that the sum of all percentages listed is 100%. Discuss the use of circle graphs to display data that describe parts of a whole.

② Introduce the concept of calculating the percent of a number. Students familiar with the connections between fractions, decimals, and percents can calculate the percent of a number by converting the percent into a decimal and multiplying it by the number. For example, to find 35% of 80, think of 35% as 35/100 or 0.35. Multiply 0.35 by 80 to find that 35% of 80 is 28. Students who are familiar with ratios and proportions can set up a proportion such as $35/100 = x/80$ and solve for x.

Have students complete item 6 of Step A. Since it is rare to find broken or half pieces of candy, explain that students may round up or down to show whole candies. Since rounding can introduce errors, explain that they must be sure to check the total by adding.

③ Have students complete Step B. You may want to have students bring in M&M's and repeat the process by using the data collected from their own bags of candy.

Extension

According to M&M/Mars, the candies are mixed in large quantities using the official color percentages. Discuss with students why small samples will vary more than large samples. Go to the following Web site to conduct your own class experiment using M&M's and compare your results with other classrooms around the world.

Mighty M&M Math Experiment
URL: http://www.iphysique.com/school/main.htm

100% M&M s

NAME:_____

DATE:_____

Step   A

Have you ever opened a bag of M&M's and wondered why there weren't the same number of red and yellow candies? People at the M&M/Mars candy company will tell you that not all colors are treated equally. Go to the following Web site and click *Color Combinations* to find out what percentage of each color there should be in a bag.

   M&M/Mars
   URL: http://www.m-ms.com/faq/

1. Use the circle graph showing the colors in Plain M&M's. List the colors and the percentages for each in order from greatest to least. If some colors are treated equally, then their order doesn't matter.

Color	Percent

2. What is the sum of all percentages listed?

   _____

3. Which color(s) should there be the most of in a bag? The least?

   _____

4. Name two colors that make up half of all colors used.

   _____

100% M&M's

Permission granted to photocopy for classroom use only. ©1998 Classroom Connect 1-(800) 638-1639 URL: http://www.classroom.com

5. Is the combined amount of red and yellow candies greater than or less than 1/2?

_____

6. Suppose a bag has 60 candies in it. How many of each color should there be?

Color	Number of Candies

Step B

Many people have put the percentages from M&M/Mars to the test. They have found that the color combinations vary from bag to bag and the total number of candies in each bag varies as well.

Suppose you counted the number of each color in a bag with 54 candies. You found 13 brown, 12 red, 11 yellow, 6 blue, 8 orange, and 4 green candies.

Calculate the percent of each color included in your bag. Compare these percentages to those you found on the M&M/Mars Web site and describe what you notice.

Color	Percent Found
Brown	
Red	
Yellow	
Blue	
Orange	
Green	

_____

_____

100% M&M's

Permission granted to photocopy for classroom use only. ©1998 Classroom Connect 1-(800) 638-1639 URL: http://www.classroom.com

LEMONADE STAND

Overview

In this lesson, students will use what they know about temperature as well as adding and multiplying money amounts to run a lemonade stand. They will use information to make predictions. Students will get a real-world look at expenses and profits in business.

Time Frame

One 45-minute session

Objectives

- Apply math skills to real-world problems.
- Make predictions based on available information.
- Learn about basic principles of expenses, revenue, and profit.

Materials

- Computer with Internet access

Procedure

1 Before beginning the activity review concepts such as temperature in Fahrenheit and Celsius and skills such as adding and multiplying money amounts. Explain the use of percents to describe the chance of rain in a weather forecast.

Introduce students to the following terms that are used throughout the activity.

Expense   The amount of money spent by a business. Examples of expenses include money spent on advertising or on producing items to sell.

Revenue   Total amount of money made from sales.

Profit   Amount of revenue left once expenses are subtracted.

❷ You may wish to organize students into pairs or small groups for this activity. Have students go to the following Web site to begin the Lemonade Stand Game.

The Lemonade Stand Game
URL: http://www.littlejason.com/lemonade/index.html

A description of the game as well as some helpful business hints are available on this page. Students who are ready to begin should click *Start Game*. Have them enter their name or the name of their group to register. Students should read the game scenario carefully to be sure they understand the rules. Once they have started the game, remind students to complete the business journal entries for each day. Suggest that they write notes and observations about what happened that day and what they might do differently next time. Students should use this information to help them make predictions on other days.

Have students keep their lemonade stands open for at least 5 days before "retiring." Students who go broke before this time should try the game again using what they learned from the first attempt. Once students have completed the activity, have them write reports that describe how much they earned as well as how they made decisions each day.

LEMONADE STAND

NAME: _____

DATE: _____

Have you ever wanted to run your own business? Go to the following Web site to open your own lemonade stand.

The Lemonade Stand Game
URL: http://www.littlejason.com/lemonade/index.html

For this activity, keep your stand open for 5 days or more. Try to make as much money as you can. Record what you do each day in your business journal. Use the results from previous days to help you make decisions.

Business Journal	Business Journal
Day _____	Day _____
Current Cash _____	Current Cash _____
Today's Forecast	Today's Forecast
Temperature _____ Chance of Rain _____	Temperature _____ Chance of Rain _____
Daily Plan	Daily Plan
Cups to Make _____	Cups to Make _____
Cost per Cup _____	Cost per Cup _____
Advertising _____	Advertising _____
Expenses	Expenses
Cup Expense _____	Cup Expense _____
Advertising _____	Advertising _____
Rent _____	Rent _____
Total Expenses _____	Total Expenses _____
Cups Sold _____	Cups Sold _____
Total Revenue _____	Total Revenue _____
Profit _____	Profit _____
Other Notes: _____	Other Notes: _____
_____	_____

Permission granted to photocopy for classroom use only. ©1998 Classroom Connect 1-(800) 638-1639 URL: http://www.classroom.com

Business Journal

Day _____

Current Cash _____

Today's Forecast

Temperature _____   Chance of Rain _____

Daily Plan

  Cups to Make _____

  Cost per Cup _____

  Advertising _____

Expenses

  Cup Expense _____

  Advertising _____

  Rent _____

                  Total Expenses _____

Cups Sold _____

                  Total Revenue _____

                       Profit _____

Other Notes: _____

_____

Business Journal

Day _____

Current Cash _____

Today's Forecast

Temperature _____   Chance of Rain _____

Daily Plan

  Cups to Make _____

  Cost per Cup _____

  Advertising _____

Expenses

  Cup Expense _____

  Advertising _____

  Rent _____

                  Total Expenses _____

Cups Sold _____

                  Total Revenue _____

                       Profit _____

Other Notes: _____

_____

Business Journal

Day _____

Current Cash _____

Today's Forecast

Temperature _____   Chance of Rain _____

Daily Plan

  Cups to Make _____

  Cost per Cup _____

  Advertising _____

Expenses

  Cup Expense _____

  Advertising _____

  Rent _____

                  Total Expenses _____

Cups Sold _____

                  Total Revenue _____

                       Profit _____

Other Notes: _____

_____

Business Journal

Day _____

Current Cash _____

Today's Forecast

Temperature _____   Chance of Rain _____

Daily Plan

  Cups to Make _____

  Cost per Cup _____

  Advertising _____

Expenses

  Cup Expense _____

  Advertising _____

  Rent _____

                  Total Expenses _____

Cups Sold _____

                  Total Revenue _____

                       Profit _____

Other Notes: _____

_____

Permission granted to photocopy for classroom use only. ©1998 Classroom Connect 1-(800) 638-1639 URL: http://www.classroom.com

Answer Key

Activity Sheet 1: Dinosaur Number Hunt
Step B

1. 59; 15; gizzard stones

2. 20; horn

3. 20; 9; bone

4. plant; 26

5. small bony plates; 53

6. ostrich; plants; meat; 8; 14

7. 3; face; 29; 12

8. meat; 46; 18; 6; 4; 6

Activity Sheet 2: Greater and Lesser Animals
Step A

1.	<	2.	>	3.	<
4.	>	5.	=	6.	>
7.	<	8.	<	9.	=

16.   11, 12, 17, 26, 32

17.   33, 35, 42, 48, 53

18.   55, 59, 61, 64, 67

Step B

Animal	Length	Weight
Humpback Whale	50-60 feet	45 tons or 90,000 pounds
Beluga	18 feet	3,500 pounds
Bottlenose Dolphin	10 feet	450 pounds
Green Sea Turtle	5 feet	850 pounds
Killer Whale	26-30 feet	5-9 tons or 10,000-18,000 pounds
Sea Otter	5 feet	45-60 pounds
Great White Shark	21 feet	7,000 pounds

Step C

1. Killer whale

2. Humpback whale

3. Killer whale or humpback whale

4. The lengths of the sea otter and the green sea turtle are equal.

5. Sea otter, bottlenose dolphin, green sea turtle, beluga, great white shark, killer whale, humpback whale

Activity Sheet 3: Ancient Number Bingo

1.	III	2.	VIII	3.	X
4.	XXIV	5.	XXXIX	6.	LI

7.   Roman numerals shown on bingo cards will vary.

Permission granted to photocopy for classroom use only. ©1998 Classroom Connect   1-(800) 638-1639   URL: http://www.classroom.com

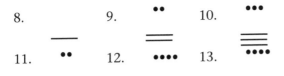

8.   9. ••   10. •••
     ___   ___   ___
             ___   ___
                        ___

11. ••   12. ••••   13. ••••
    ___   ___   ___

14. Mayan numbers shown on bingo cards will vary.

15.   16.   17.

15. || 16. ∩ || 17. ∩∩ |||

18. ℮∩   19. ℮℮ || 20. ∩∩∩∩∩ |||
                 || |||

Activity Sheet 4: Addition and Subtraction Monster Stories
Step A
1. Subtract; 15 – 6 = 9 cookies left

2. Subtract; 12 – 7 = 5 more toes than Zondi

3. Add; 8 + 4 = 12 moon rocks

4. Subtract; 16 – 8 = 8 fingers

Activity Sheet 5: Pyramid Pictographs
Check students' work as pictographs will vary. Make sure the keys at the bottom of the pictographs are complete.

Activity Sheet 6: Planet Graph
Step A
1. Mercury, 0; Venus, 0; Earth, 1; Mars, 2; Jupiter, 16; Saturn, 18; Uranus, 15; Neptune, 8; Pluto, 1

2. Check students' bar graphs. Be sure graphs include labels for each axis as well as titles.

Step B
1. Saturn

2. Mercury and Venus

3. 15 more moons

4. Pluto

Activity Sheet 7: Musical Multiplication
Step A
1.

×	1	2	3	4	5	6	7	8	9
1	1	2	3	4	5	6	7	8	9
2	2	4	6	8	10	12	14	16	18
3	3	6	9	12	15	18	21	24	27
4	4	8	12	16	20	24	28	32	36
5	5	10	15	20	25	30	35	40	45
6	6	12	18	24	30	36	42	48	54
7	7	14	21	28	35	42	49	56	63
8	8	16	24	32	40	48	56	64	72
9	9	18	27	36	45	54	63	72	81

Permission granted to photocopy for classroom use only. ©1998 Classroom Connect   1-(800) 638-1639   URL: http://www.classroom.com

2. Possible answers shown.

    2s: Products skip count by 2; all even numbers.

    3s: Products skip count by 3; products alternate between even and odd numbers; sum of digits in each product is 3, 6, or 9

    4s: Products skip count by 4; products are every other even number beginning with 4

    5s: Products skip count by 5; products of odd numbers end in 5 and products of even numbers end in 0.

    6s: Products skip count by 6; sum of digits in each product is 6, 3, or 9.

    7s: Products skip count by 7; products alternate between even and odd numbers.

    8s: Products skip count by 8; ones digits repeat 8, 6, 4, 2, 0.

    9s: Products skip count by 9; sum of digits in each product is 9; tens digit increases by 1 and ones digit decreases by 1.

Activity Sheet 8: Folding Shapes

1. Possible answer: squares, rectangles, and triangles

2.

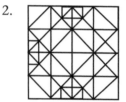

Activity Sheet 9: Shapely Fractions

Step A

1. Hexagon

2. Trapezoid

3. Rhombus

4. Triangle

Step B

Answers to questions 1–10 are available at the following Web site.

URL: http://math.rice.edu/~lanius/Patterns/answers.html

Activity Sheet 10: Abacus Addition

		10	5	1
1.	4	0	0	4
2.	7	0	1	2
3.	11	1	0	1
4.	5	0	1	0
5.	20	2	0	0
6.	16	1	1	1

7–16 Check students drawings. Students may choose to show only those beads moved to the center bar.

Permission granted to photocopy for classroom use only. ©1998 Classroom Connect 1-(800) 638-1639 URL: http://www.classroom.com

13. 74   14. 69   15. 118   16. 159

Activity Sheet 11: Using Common Cents
Step A
1. $0.55   2. $0.37   3. $1.16   4. $2.65   5. $3.79   6.$0.48

7. $0.21   8. $0.82   9–11. Answers will vary.

Step B: Possible combinations of coins and bills shown.

	Cost of Item	Paid With	Amount of Change	Pennies	Nickels	Dimes	Quarters	$1 Bills
1.	$0.36	$1.00	$0.64	4	0	1	2	0
				4	1	3	1	0
				4	0	6	0	0
2.	$0.83	$1.00	$0.17	2	1	1	0	0
				2	3	0	0	0
				17	0	0	0	0
3.	$3.45	$5.00	$1.55	0	1	0	2	1
				0	1	5	0	1
				5	0	5	4	0
4.	$1.57	$5.00	$3.43	3	1	1	1	3
				3	1	1	5	2
				3	0	4	0	3
5.	$2.92	$5.00	$2.08	3	1	0	0	2
				8	0	0	4	1
				3	1	0	4	1
6.	$1.64	$2.00	$0.36	1	0	1	1	0
				1	1	3	0	0
				1	2	0	1	0

Activity Sheet 12: Heads or Tails?
Answers will vary.

Activity Sheet 13: Patterns with Numbers
Step A
55; 89; 144; 233

Step B
4. 1, 1, 2, 3, 5, 8, 13; Possible answer: The side lengths follow the Fibonacci sequence.

5. Possible answer: If quarter spirals are drawn through each of these squares in order, the complete spiral resembles the spirals found in some sea shells.

Activity Sheet 14: Multiplication Magic
Step A
1. 1,800   2. 24,000   3. 2,800   4. 15,000   5. 18,000

6. 480,000   7. 320,000   8. 3,500,000   9. 900,000

Step C
1. 184   2. 1,260   3. 385   4. 1,836   5. 30,420   6. 87

7. Possible answer: $90 \times 3 = 270$ and $4 \times 3 = 12$ so $270 + 12 = 282$

8. Possible answer: $7 \times 50 = 350$ so $350 - 7 = 343$

Permission granted to photocopy for classroom use only. ©1998 Classroom Connect   1-(800) 638-1639   URL: http://www.classroom.com

Activity Sheet 15: Multicultural Multiplication
Step B

Groups of 24	Egyptian Number	Total
1	⋂⋂ ∥ ∥	24
2	⋂⋂⋂⋂ ∥∥∥	48
4	⋂⋂⋂⋂ ⋂⋂⋂⋂⋂ ∥∥∥ ∥∥∥	96

1. 24 + 48 = 72

2. 48 + 96 = 144

Activity Sheet 16: Estimating Costs
Step A

1. $4.00   2. $8.50   3. $3.60   4. $5.70   5. $8.05   6. $5.08

7. $11.46   8. $8.97   9. $5.70; no   10. $4.80; yes   11. $5.30; no   12. $4.50; yes

Step B

Name of Food Group	Number of Servings per Day
Bread, Cereal, Rice and Pasta	6-11 servings
Vegetable	3-5 servings
Fruit	2-3 servings
Meat, Poultry, Fish, Dry Beans and Peas, Eggs, and Nuts	2-4 servings
Milk, Yogurt, and Cheese	2-3 servings

Activity Sheet 17: The Iditarod Dog Sled Race

Answers for the activities can be found at the following Web site.

URL: http://www.pbs.org/learn/mathline/concepts/feb98/conceptsanswers.html.

Activity Sheet 18: Athletes' Averages
Step A

1. Median = 34; Mean = 32.8   2. Answers will vary.

Step B

1. 7 receptions in 1997; Possible answer: The number of receptions during this season is much lower than any other season.

2. Answers shown are based on data for seasons from 1985–1997.

	Using Data from All Seasons Played	Using Data Without Outlier(s)
Median	84	85
Mean	81	87.5

ANSWER KEY

Permission granted to photocopy for classroom use only. ©1998 Classroom Connect 1-(800) 638-1639 URL: http://www.classroom.com

3. Possible answer: The outlier decreased the mean by 6.5 receptions per season while it only decreased the median by 1 reception per season.

4. Possible answer: The median is a better description of the data since outliers don't affect it as much as the mean.

Step C

1. 408 points in 1985; 457 points in 1994

2. Answers shown are based on data for seasons from 1984–1997.

	Using Data from All Seasons Played	Using Data Without Outlier(s)
Median	2,491	2,541
Mean	2,252.1	2,582.9

3. Possible answer: The median is a better description of the data since it only decreased by 50 points per season when the outliers were included. The mean on the other hand decreased by almost 331 points per season.

Activity Sheet 19: Snowflake Geometry
Step B

1. Answers will vary.

2. All snowflakes should have 3 lines of symmetry.

3. When snowflakes are opened completely, all folds are lines of symmetry.

4. Descriptions will vary.

Activity Sheet 20: Patterns and Tessellations
Step A

1. flip   2. slide   3. turn   4. flip

Activity Sheet 21: Islamic Patterns
Step A

Part of the Circle	Label
radius	AC
diameter	BE
chord	CD
center point	A

Activity Sheet 22: Tangram Math
Step A

Pictures of square arrangements may vary.

Step B

1. 1/4   2. 1/8   3. 1/16   4. 2/16 or 1/8   5. 2/16 or 1/8

6. 1/2   7. 1/4   8. 2/4 or 1/2   9. 2/4 or 1/2

Step C

1. 1/2 square units   2. 1 square unit   3. 2 square units   4. 1 square unit

Permission granted to photocopy for classroom use only. ©1998 Classroom Connect 1-(800) 638-1639 URL: http://www.classroom.com

Activity 24: Fractions and Food
Step A

1.

Number of Batches	Original recipe serves...				
	4 people	5 people	6 people	7 people	8 people
2	8	10	12	14	16
3	12	15	18	21	24
4	16	20	24	28	32
5	20	25	30	35	40
6	24	30	36	42	48

2. 4 batches   3. 4 batches   4. 4 batches   5. 5 batches

Activity Sheet 25: Measurable Improvements
Answers will vary.

Activity Sheet 26: Allowable Percents
1. About 3/4   2. About 4/5   3. About 1/2   4. 1/10

5. About 3/4; about 1/2   6. About 2/3

Activity Sheet 27: 100% M&M's
Step A

1. Brown, 30%; Red, 20%; Yellow, 20%; Blue, 10%; Green, 10%; Orange, 10%

2. 100%

3. Brown; Blue, Green, or Orange

4. Possible answers: brown and red, or brown and yellow.

5. Less than 1/2

6. Brown, 18; Red, 12; Yellow, 12; Blue, 6; Green, 6; Orange, 6

Step B

Brown, 24%; Red, 22%; Yellow, 20%; Blue, 11%; Orange, 15%; Green, 7%

Permission granted to photocopy for classroom use only. ©1998 Classroom Connect   1-(800) 638-1639   URL: http://www.classroom.com

LIST OF SUPPLEMENTAL WEB SITES

RESOURCES FOR REAL-WORLD APPLICATIONS

Sea World's Animal Bytes
URL: http://www.seaworld.org/animal_bytes/animal_bytes.html

Animals Around the World
URL: http://www.chicojr.chico.k12.ca.us/staff/gray/animals.html

Knowledge Adventure Encyclopedia
URL: http://www.adventure.com/encyclopedia

The Borden Teacher Zone: Animals from A to Z Lesson Finder
URL: http://www.bordenteacherzone.com/series/frame/frame.htm

Enchanted Learning: Zoom Dinosaurs
URL: http://www.EnchantedLearning.com/subjects/dinosaurs

Dragonfly Web Pages: Virtual Dinosaur Dig
URL: http://www.muohio.edu/dragonfly/skeletons/dig.htmlx

Natural History Museum: Cats! Wild to Mild
URL: http://www.lam.mus.ca.us/cats/

The Tiger Information Center: Cubs 'n Kids
URL: http://www.5tigers.org/cubs.htm

WhaleNet Internet Resources: Marine Mammal Links and Information
URL: http://whale.wheelock.edu/whalenet-stuff/interwhale.html

The Nine Planets: A Multimedia Tour of the Solar System
URL: http://seds.lpl.arizona.edu/billa/tnp/

Welcome to the Planets
URL: http://pds.jpl.nasa.gov/planets/

Athena, Earth, Space, and Science for K–12
URL: http://athena.wednet.edu/index.html

StarChild Learning Center for Young Astronomers
URL: http://starchild.gsfc.nasa.gov/docs/StarChild/StarChild.html

Project SkyMath
URL: http://www.unidata.ucar.edu/staff/blynds/Skymath.html

Sports Illustrated for Kids
URL: http://www.pathfinder.com/SIFK/

The Official Site of Major League Baseball
URL: http://www.majorleaguebaseball.com/

Permission granted to photocopy for classroom use only. ©1998 Classroom Connect 1-(800) 638-1639 URL: http://www.classroom.com

The Official Site of the National Basketball Association
URL: http://www.nba.com/

The Official Site of the National Football League
URL: http://www.nfl.com/

What Machine Could Do All of This?
URL: http://www.favachiro.com/files/machine.htm

The Roller Coaster Database
URL: http://roller.coaster.net/

U.S. Bureau of the Census: National POPClock
URL: http://www.census.gov/cgi-bin/popclock

The World Clock
URL: http://www.stud.ntnu.no/USERBIN/steffent/verdensur.pl

Distance Finder
URL: http://www.indo.com/distance

Yahoo! Travel
URL: http://travel.yahoo.com/destinations

MATH FUN AND GAMES

Math Baseball
URL: http://www.funbrain.com/math/

Flash Cards
URL: http://www.infomath.com/html/practice.html

Number and Word Puzzles
URL: http://www1.tpgi.com.au/users/puzzles/index.html

Pattern Blocks
URL: http://www.best.com/~ejad/java/patterns/patterns_j.shtml

Questacon: Puzzlequest
URL: http://sunsite.anu.edu/au/Questacon/pq_main.html

Tangram Puzzles - Set 1
URL: http://www.ex.ac.uk/cimt/puzzles/tangrams/tangset1.htm

MATH AND ART

Learning with Origami
URL: http://ccwf.cc.utexas.edu/~vbeatty/origami/learning/index.html

How to Fold a Crane
URL: http://www.rose.brandeis.eud/users/peisach/howcrane.html

Joseph Wu's Origami Page
URL: http://www.origami.vancouver.bc.ca/index.html

Permission granted to photocopy for classroom use only. ©1998 Classroom Connect 1-(800) 638-1639 URL: http://www.classroom.com

Fractions and Paper Folding
URL: http://www.iit.edu/~smile/ma9320.html

Tessellation Tutorials
URL: http://forum.swarthmore.edu/sum95/suzanne/tess.intro.html

Tessellations by Carol Sulik
URL: http://www.inform.umd.edu:8080/UMS+State/UMD-Projects/
　　MCTP/Technology/School_WWW_Pages/Tessellations/1996Project/
　　TitlePage.html

M.C. Escher's Life
URL: http://library.advanced.org/11750/escherlife.shtml

M.C. Escher Collection
URL: http://gauss.technion.ac.il/~rl/M.C.Escher/

The World of Escher
URL: http://lonestar.texas.net/~escher/

The Art of Oriental Carpets
URL: http://forum.swarthmore.edu/geometry/rugs/

MATH HISTORY

Mathematics Archives WWW Server
URL: http://archives.math.utk.edu/index.html

History of Mathematics by Subject
URL: http://aleph0.clarku.edu/~djoyce/mathhist/subjects.html

Links to Information on Numbers Systems
URL: http://forum.swarthmore.edu/alejandre/numerals.html

Roman Numeral Converter
URL: http://www.ivtech.com/roman/

Mayan Numbers
URL: http://www.vpds.wsu.edu/fair_95/gym/UM001.html

Vedic Square
URL: http://www.amulet.co.uk/symbols/kamea/vedic.html

Leonardo Pisano Fibonacci
URL: http://www-groups.dcs.st-and.ac.uk/~history/Mathematicians/
　　Fibonacci.html

Fibonacci Numbers and the Golden Section
URL: http://www.mcs.surrey.ac.uk/Personal/R.Knott/Fibonacci/fib.html

RESOURCES

Ask Dr. Math
URL: http://forum.swarthmore.edu/dr.math/

Permission granted to photocopy for classroom use only. ©1998 Classroom Connect   1-(800) 638-1639   URL: http://www.classroom.com

Eisenhower National Clearinghouse for Mathematics and Science Education
URL: http://www.enc.org/

Math Forum: Elementary School Student Center
URL: http://forum.swarthmore.edu/students/elem/

Internet Resources for Elementary Mathematics Educators
URL: http://www.math.ttu.edu/~dmettler/title.html

K–12 Educator's Roadmap to the Internet: Math and Science
URL: http://150.216.8.1/roadmap/scimath.htm

Web Sites and Resources for Teachers: Math
URL: http://www.csun.edu/~vceed009/math.html

IBM Education: K-12 Weblinks
URL: http://www.solutions.ibm.com/k12/weblink/links.html

PBS Mathline
URL: http://www.pbs.org/learn/mathline/concepts/concepts.html

Plane Math
URL: http://www.planemath.com/activities/pmactivitiesall.html

Energy Conservation Enhancement Project: Mathematics
URL: http://ecep1.usl.edu/ecep/math/math.htm

Encarta Lesson Collection: K–12 Mathematics
URL: http://encarta.msn.com/schoolhouse/lessons/results.asp?subject=Mathematics

The Explorer
URL: http://explorer.scrtec.org/explorer/

INDICES

Berit's Best Sites for Kids
URL: http://db.cochran.com/li_toc:theoPage.db

4Kids Treehouse
URL: http://www.4kids.com

Oz Kidz Cubby House: An Early Childhood Cyber Centre
URL: http://www.ozkidz.gil.com.au/cubbyhouse/

Kid Info...School Subjects
URL: http://www.kidinfo.com/School_Subjects.html

The Mining Co. Guides
URL: http://home.miningco.com/family/mbody.htm#kids

Loogootee Elementary West: Sites to See
URL: http://www.siec.k12.in.us/~west/sites/index.html

Permission granted to photocopy for classroom use only. ©1998 Classroom Connect   1-(800) 638-1639   URL: http://www.classroom.com